YIN & YANG
Nutrition for Dogs
Maximizing Health with Whole Foods, Not Drugs

By Judy Morgan DVM and Hue Grant

Disclaimer

The information in this book is provided in good faith; however, no guarantee or warranty is given. Since the health of each pet and quality of ingredients used is unpredictable, results may vary. The content provided in this book is presented for information purposes only and is not meant to replace examination and diagnosis by your veterinarian. Please consult with your veterinarian before making any dietary changes for your pet.

THIRTY · SIX
PAWS
P R E S S

www.drjudymorgan.com

TABLE OF CONTENTS

DEDICATION

This book is dedicated to all the wonderful dogs that I have had the honor to meet during my career. Each and every one has taught me valuable lessons about the ability to live, love, forgive, and heal from within, when given the opportunity. They make my life whole by allowing me to serve them.

-Judy Morgan

In particular, we are thankful for Myra, the Cavachon on the front cover. She came to us as a broken-hearted, medically challenged, six-year-old, from a family that could no longer care for her. She allowed us to heal her body and soul, and in the process, stole our hearts and touched the lives of people everywhere. She was funny and fun-loving; her antics with squeaky dinosaurs will always be remembered. Sadly, she crossed the rainbow bridge in November 2016, but she will live in our hearts forever.

-Judy Morgan & Hue Grant

ACKNOWLEDGEMENTS

First and foremost, I am thankful for all the pet owners who have allowed me to work with their wonderful dogs that have taught me so much over the years. Every patient has contributed to my knowledge base, while forgiving my mistakes along the way.

My husband, Hue Grant, has suffered through long days and nights, rewrites, and the takeover of his kitchen while testing and photographing recipes. In a moment of brilliance (or a blind squirrel finding the nut, as he likes to say), he came up with the title for this book.

The people who were kind enough to offer advice, edits, and clarification gave invaluable feedback; their willingness to be brutal was welcome! Thank you, David Brock, for keeping my facts straight and reminding me to add pancreas. Thanks to Annette Desautels for being a novice willing to take a stab at deciphering the needs of your Cavalier King Charles spaniel, Mackenzie, and nailing it! Emilie Rhodes, you will always be remembered as the person who enlightened me that not all slow cookers are Crock Pots. You were also the only person that noticed I forgot to put in any instructions other than the ingredients on the last meal. I was so excited to finish the last recipe, I totally blew through it! Barbara Sheridan, you are the queen of punctuation and grammar. I probably should have paid more attention in high school English class.

Finally, thank you Michele Allen, founder of Monkey's House Senior Dog Hospice and Sanctuary. You constantly challenge me; you have been my best student. I'm grateful for the green tripe recipes and first aid for the freezer. Only someone living with two dozen senior dogs understands the importance of being prepared for anything. I am honored to have been chosen to care for this wonderful group of dogs. Thank you, Paula Sifford, for finding Scout and Freckles, the two seniors that got us moving forward with Michele's amazing and wonderful idea, even if they never did make it all the way to Monkey's House.

TESTIMONIALS

I have started applying some of the basic principles to get a handle on itching in my two dogs. The addition of more cooling proteins, along with reducing the hot proteins, has brought remarkable results! The dog's itching is minimal. I look forward to my consult to further refine their diet/supplement regimen.

-Julie Rider

After our consultation I implemented the recommendation to add raw pork and goat milk. I've noticed less licking of the hind end, decreased odor around the eyes, and a better tongue color. She really loves the food and is excited to eat every day.

-Debbie Schwartz

My dog suffered from itching, frequent burping, and vomiting. After speaking with you, reading your books, and watching your webinars and videos, I started cooking for him following TCVM guidelines. I didn't know I was feeding him exactly the opposite of what a warm dog should be eating! After changing proteins, his itching disappeared within two weeks and all medications were eliminated! His tummy issues resolved. He was not as snarly and seemed happier. His little pink nose started to return to the black patent leather it should be. His weight decreased from 11.1 pounds to 8.3 pounds in ten weeks! He's slim and trim and a ball of energy. I'm feeding him twice the volume of food he was getting before. I am amazed at the difference feeding whole, real, freshly prepared food, that is right for your particular pet, makes! Every pet owner needs this information!

-Ruth Ackerman

After reading "Needles to Natural", I selected Dr. Judy Morgan to treat my Cocker Spaniel with severe allergies. I had no knowledge of Chinese Medicine, but was in limbo, having declined food and drugs offered by the dermatologist. Dr. Morgan's compassion for animals, healing and teaching, combined with her vast knowledge of Traditional and Chinese Medicine is impressive. Dr. Morgan has helped me to be more confident in preparing healthy meals, snacks and supplements for Amy!

-Faith Jones

Two years ago, I contacted Dr. Morgan when Bear was diagnosed with rib osteosarcoma. I cannot thank her enough for teaching me about nutrition and Chinese medicine. During this time, I not only learned so much for my dogs, I have even changed my diet. Kudos and thanks for sharing her knowledge.

A very thankful – Deb Sawyer and Bear

I know how much real food has made a difference in both of my dogs' lives. For three years I applied Tacrolimus drops daily to the eyes of my Cavalier, Riley, for his dry eye. When I bought From Needles to Natural, the first thing I tried was the diet for dry eye, in hopes of getting him off the drops. It worked! While the drops helped, they weren't the answer. Fresh meat, clams, sardines, spinach, eggs, carrots, and pears were what his body needed to naturally heal his goop-filled eyes. Within three to four months he was off the drops, I couldn't be happier. Kaden, my other Cavalier, had really sparse fur and his nails hardly ever grew. He now has a full Cavalier coat and his nails need to be trimmed just as often as his brother Riley's. This may not sound like a good thing, but I know that it is. He was obviously missing some very important nutrients. I really enjoy preparing their meals and watching their anticipation. Those bowls are licked almost dishwasher-clean. They are off kibble for good and we are never looking back.

-Barbara Hammond

Our older dog, Bijou, was diagnosed with leaky gut. I slowly weaned her onto a novel raw protein diet. She thrived and acted like a pup, with never another episode of HGE, bloody stool or any problems for the rest of her life. The vet had said she would likely have these episodes about every other month. Nope. Never again. NEVER AGAIN!! We added all manner of different proteins and she handled them all like a pro. It made a believer out of my skeptical husband, who wasn't sure we were doing the right thing. He has become an avid proponent of raw diets for dogs, as have I. Real food makes all the difference. ALL the difference.

-Jeri Howell

Our Havanese puppy was sick with slow weight gain, vomiting, diarrhea, and food refusal since we brought him home at eight weeks. He was eating kibble from the breeder. Each time his stomach troubles would peak, we would give him pumpkin, chicken, and rice, but he only seemed to get worse. He was in the hospital twice for vomiting and once because he was vomiting blood. This went on until he was nine months old. That was when we switched his diet. Within a week we saw a huge change. He was a different dog. This pup has such a sensitive stomach and without this change to real food, I don't know where he would be today.

-Jill Iovino & Scrappy Doo

Two years ago, my cattle dog Sophie, was diagnosed with liver cancer. I was told I had roughly a month with her. She was bloated and miserable. I started feeding a home prepared diet to support her liver. She lived for another year and a half. She was 14 years old and looked 100% better in the end, than when we started.

-Karen Smith

My 14-year-old Sheltie, Annie, had high liver enzymes on her annual test (ALT 1200). I immediately started a home prepared liver support diet with added herbs and honey. Her levels dropped within six months; now her ALT is 40!

-Karen Smith

My Border collie, Spud, was fed strictly kibble for the first ten years of his life. He was so arthritic and in pain, he could hardly get up from lying down. His eyes were sad, his coat was dull, and he smelled horrible. When I adopted two Cavalier puppies, I started feeding them a raw diet. I also changed Spud to raw food. What a remarkable difference this made for him! Today, at 11 years old, he keeps up with the puppies, has no issues getting up, his eyes are bright, his nose is like patent leather, his coat is shiny with no doggy smell, and he had no fleas or ticks this summer. But most of all, he is happy again and loving life!

-Phyllis Harrison Gorzynski

My Yorkie, Gracie, was diagnosed with stage one kidney disease. I was feeding her kibble. I spent endless nights looking into pet nutrition; it can become overwhelming. When I switched Gracie to a raw diet, her blood values went up a little. The vet mentioned a prescription diet. I said I was not comfortable with that, so I added whole food and herbs to her meals. With her new diet, her values came down and one is back to normal. She has lots of energy and runs like a tiny racehorse. She is happy and healthy; she'll turn 14 soon. She is the light of my life, and I really believe my food and supplement choices have made a difference.

-Suzanne Brusseau

My English Springer Spaniel, Kodi, was diagnosed with kidney failure at age eight, given only six months to live. The vet wanted me to start feeding a prescription diet. Honestly, it was too expensive for a picky eater that I knew she wouldn't touch it, so I started my research, which landed me on a raw diet consisting of all «people» foods. During the diet change, her eyes were noticeably brighter, her coat became thick and shiny, and her once dry, gray nose was back to being soft and black. Six months later, all kidney and liver function tests were within NORMAL ranges! I firmly believe that this would not have happened without the change to a "real food" diet. Kodi made it to age ten. Real food gave me two more years with my girl.

-Renee Ayers

After learning about the energetics of food from Dr. Judy, I adjusted my dog's diet and the changes were amazing. By feeding a fresh, whole food diet, geared for each dog's issues, I now have non-itchy, calm, shiny dogs!

-Julie D.

We bought my daughter a Maltese puppy. He had Giardia. He was treated with two medications, as well as a heartworm preventative on the same day. A few hours later, he became violently ill. He was only 2.8 pounds at the time. Blood tests revealed high liver enzymes. I started him on a raw diet, added probiotics and vitamins, as well as a liver support supplement. After months of having a damaged liver, it is healed and back to normal. I learned a big lesson on how important food and supplements are for good health.

-Lisa T.

I first decided to cook for our cavalier, Hunter, out of desperation. He had been on kibble mixed with cooked ground meat most of his life. As soon as his immune system began being crippled by the medications he was taking for his epilepsy, heart, and thyroid, I knew I had to do whatever it would take to improve his appetite and well-being. I truly believe that by feeding him Dr. Morgan's puploaf recipe, he regained his strength and vitality for the remaining months he was with us. Food therapy does work; it improves a pet's ability to stay strong. It also helps the pet owners know that they are doing everything they can to keep their pets as healthy as possible.

-Judy Heath

My Pomeranian, Dewey, suffered for six years with an undiagnosed and incurable autoimmune disease. Traditional veterinarians offered repeated rounds of antibiotics, pain medications, and prescription kibble, but the problem continued. After spending $50,000, I discovered Dr. Judy Morgan. She went through Dewey's history and offered me all the tools to learn, as well as truly understand, the benefits of Chinese medicine. She gave me a detailed diet of home cooked recipes with a goal in mind that food and supplements would help keep Dewey's immune system strong, decreasing the need to use antibiotics. Her diet recommendations were easy to follow, easily explained in her books. My three Pomeranians were in heaven with the delicious food!

It has now been almost two years since I sought out Dr. Judy's guidance. Dewey, within the first six months had made drastic, noticeable changes. His fur was softer, thicker, and had that shine we all admire. His energy increased; he was playful again. His weight dropped almost seven pounds to an ideal weight. His personality blossomed to what a happy, healthy dog is expected to be. His autoimmune disorder will never be cured, but we certainly can manage it, as well as minimize his flare ups all with the proper foods. I now home cook for all three of my dogs, as well as every foster that comes into my care. The real difference is seen when you have a puppy mill dog that has only been fed poor quality kibble food. The improvement in their coats, mobility, skin, and ear infections is dramatic. That is pure bliss when you truly make a difference in a dog's life.

-Tammy Howard

My husband and I adopted two Golden Retrievers from a rescue in Minnesota. They came severely overweight, arthritic, and out of shape at six and seven years old. I transitioned them to raw feeding and immediately saw huge improvements in body composition, muscle strength, mobility, and elimination of hot spots. We lost both dogs the same year, but they were 16 and 17. Neither dog ever had surgery, tooth extractions, or any major illness until plain old age took them. I am so grateful for those who empowered and taught me to take care of my boys. It gave me courage to trust my instincts and say no to disapproving vets. Now I'm the crazy dog food lady in my little world. I share whenever I can. I'm still learning, but being able to help even just one dog, is totally worth it.

-Melanie Olson

Our rescue cavalier, Miley, was suffering from severe itching and her ears were thick. Her foster mother began a recipe from your cookbook to help with the skin issues. Miley began to respond and the itching decreased. When Miley came to live with us, we continued using the recipe, modifying it slightly to add some cooling foods, as she would get heated. Miley has thrived on her home cooked food. We tweak it from time to time, but the base recipe has always been the same. She loves it! Miley is thriving on her food. Her coat is shiny and bright! Thank you for sharing your recipes and knowledge on cooling and healing foods.

-Kelly Hummert

I am convinced that starting a raw diet, with fresh foods and supplements, enabled my Katie Rose to live a high-quality life during her seemingly endless treatment for Transitional Cell Carcinoma. Shortly before this diagnosis, she had bladder stones removed and was also found to have Cushing's disease, which was successfully managed with supplements instead of drugs. With all this, I thought the deck was stacked against a quality life for any length of time. Yet Katie was a happy, active Scottie for three years after diagnosis even though her prognosis was "she might make two years if we're lucky". Her doctors were astounded, as she didn't look or act like a sick dog. Katie Rose passed in August 2017, at 12 years of age, but I know she would not have been with me very long, had it not been for a healthy diet and integrated veterinary care.

-Patricia Allsebrook

Our 8-year-old English Springer Spaniel, Sadie, was diagnosed with Chronic Lymphoid Leukemia. Her lymphocyte count was 86,000 (normal is 5,000). She was referred to an Oncologist, who confirmed the diagnosis, prescribing chemotherapy and prednisone. At that time, she was on a diet of dry kibble. When asked what dietary changes should be made for her, the Oncologist told me that I should not make any changes at all. Dr. Morgan recommended that we modify her diet to empower her body to fight the cancer itself. We began feeding Sadie raw dog food exclusively, along with the following supplements: probiotics, coconut oil, green tea extract, and fish oil. Additionally, we gave her eggs and sardines a few times a week. Two months later, her lymphocyte count was down to 36,000! At that time, Dr. Morgan recommended adding mushroom extract and CoQ10 to her diet. We have also been giving her a homemade veggie blend (spinach, kale, cabbage, garlic, ginger, red pepper, parsley, celery, etc.) with her meals. It has now been six months since her diagnosis, and Sadie remains symptom-free. We have decided not to have any more blood tests run for the time being: we'd rather spend the money on providing her a high-quality diet that she loves!

-Rachel Vail

I have 2 dogs, Beau, a 6-year-old, adopted basset hound, and Daisy, 2-year-old rough collie. Your books have enabled me to pinpoint their "type" and cook for it. Beau is a "cold" dog and Daisy is a "hot" dog. Problems were starting to arise, such as dull coats and excessive shedding, lumps, and lameness. Ten years ago, I started losing my dogs to weird cancer and illnesses I had never seen before. Dogs from my youth never had these problems. They lived long, pain-free, great lives. As an adult, all my dogs have been fed high-end kibble and canned food, but a nagging voice inside my head was questioning the dog foods when recall after recall started. I remembered my mom and grandmother cooked for their dogs. I was looking to make dog food, but the information was so confusing. I came across you one day and you made sense. Your books on the energetics of food have been a lifesaver; they are so on target. Daisy has her beautiful collie coat back. Beau is not shedding; his strange cough and sneeze have cleared using your recipes. His limping is slight and lumps are shrinking, since I have been using draining foods. Thank you!

-Gabrielle Del Corso

THE BASICS

Why Should You Prepare Food for Your Pets?

It's simple. The pet food industry has let you down. You have depended on them to provide wholesome nutrition to keep your pets healthy. They advertise ingredients as holistic, natural, and human grade; in reality, ingredients are often waste products from the human food industry or rendered meals from diseased animal carcasses.

Dry kibble is highly processed, with ingredients often cooked at high temperatures many times before landing in the bag headed for the pet food aisle. Sprayed-on fats and appetite enhancers are often rancid by the time the food makes its way to your pet's bowl. Fillers such as peanut hulls, brewer's rice, pea fiber, and dried beet pulp, with low nutrient quality, can make up a significant percentage of the processed food. It's time to stand up for your pets and offer them real food made with real ingredients that will keep them healthy. A million years ago wolves were carnivores, eating the whole carcass of the animals they killed, along with the digested vegetable matter in the gut. They could exist on vegetable matter, grass, fruits and berries, feces, and the decaying flesh of dead animals when game was scarce. Wolves were carnivorous omnivores, meaning they were opportunists, eating what was available. Wolves in the wild are still carnivores, and have not evolved to eat a diet based on cooked grain, which is the basis for many processed pet foods today.

However, when dogs and cats first became domesticated, they hunted less and ate the leftovers from human meals, often scavenging the remains of discarded animal carcasses, fruit, and vegetable matter. As evolution continued, dogs and cats became more reliant on humans to provide food. As the diet of humans changed from fresh, locally farmed foods to highly processed, industrialized foods, the canine and feline diets followed suit. Dogs and cats became less hunters and more scavengers, relying on man to supply nutrition. Suddenly, degenerative diseases like arthritis, diabetes, and cancer became more prevalent in both humans and domestic animals. While the diets of dogs and cats have changed, their genome has not, meaning they still require a diet consisting of mostly meat and bones, offal or organ meats, and a small amount of vegetable matter to thrive.

The pet food industry has spent millions of advertising and teaching dollars to convince veterinarians and the pet-owning public that the only way to provide a complete diet is to feed processed industrial food.

Unfortunately, since the advent of processed food for pets, the pandemic of degenerative health problems has escalated in dogs and cats. Veterinarians continually treat inflammatory and degenerative diseases, yet they fail to see any correlation between the highly processed diets and disease. The profession has been talked into believing that industrial food cannot possibly be a causative factor in disease. In fact, they have been taught by the major pet food companies that the only way to treat chronic disease is to prescribe more processed industrialized foods.

Many of these diets are nothing more than poor quality ingredients including by-products, combined with fillers and chemicals to "treat" disease, with minimal high-quality food included. The veterinarian sells the "solution" which leads to more problems and the cycle continues. The veterinarian and pet owner readily accept this disease cycle as normal.

Allergy symptoms and ear infections are two of the most commonly treated diseases in veterinary medicine. These are followed closely by dental disease, joint disease and arthritis, obesity, diabetes, behavioral problems, seizures, inflammatory bowel disease, pancreatitis, and cancer. These diseases have one thing in common: inflammation. Most industrial foods are highly inflammatory due to the high content of carbohydrates, gluten, preservatives, binders, dyes and chemicals.

Recently dozens of dry kibble pet foods were tested for heavy metals and were found to contain high levels of arsenic and lead. These heavy metals can lead to behavioral disorders, anxiety, seizures, and diseases of many body organs. Since pets are commonly fed the same food for months to years on end, the heavy metals continue to accumulate and damage the body.

Holistic veterinarians that recommend feeding whole food and raw food diets understand very well that processed, poor quality diets lead to degenerative diseases. Once pets are fed real food, the changes in disease patterns are nothing short of miraculous. Yet the majority of traditional veterinarians believe that home-made diets containing fresh foods, particularly raw meat and bones, are dangerous. They warn pet owners that they are risking the lives of their pets and their families by allowing their animals to eat raw meats.

The American Veterinary Medical Association (AVMA) policy states: "The AVMA discourages the feeding to cats and dogs of any animal-source protein that has not first been subjected to a process to eliminate pathogens because of the risk of illness to cats and dogs as well as humans. Cooking or pasteurization through the application of heat until the protein reaches an internal temperature adequate to destroy pathogenic organisms has been the traditional method used to eliminate pathogens in animal-source protein, although the AVMA recognizes that newer technologies and other methods such as irradiation are constantly being developed and implemented."

I'm not going to eat irradiated food and neither are my pets.

Veterinarians warn it is impossible to balance a home prepared diet: the pet will die of malnutrition or nutritional deficiencies. This is valid in rare instances where the pet owner feeds a very limited diet. I have seen pets that have been fed a home prepared diet consisting of meat and rice for years. The pets have not died of malnutrition, but they certainly were not receiving complete nutrition to help them thrive.

Pets have the ability to survive for years as long as they ingest enough calories. Thriving with optimal health requires a varied diet with a complete array of vitamins and minerals. Many pet parents would like to feed their pets home prepared diets, but are scared off by those telling horror stories of nutritional deficiencies. Many veterinary nutritionists "design" home prepared diets by choosing one protein, one carbohydrate, one fat, and a synthetic vitamin/mineral mix. In my mind, this is hardly better than feeding a processed industrial food. This scenario is similar to the pet parent that has been feeding chicken and rice for years, supplementing with processed treats containing synthetic vitamins and minerals.

The pet food industry has convinced veterinarians and pet parents the only way to achieve complete and balanced nutrition is by pouring dry kibble into a bowl. They warn against adding any home-prepared food or "leftovers", as this will make the diet "unbalanced" and make your pet sick. I don't know anyone who obsesses over planning every meal to be complete and balanced for their family, yet pet parents have been brainwashed into believing every meal for the dog or cat must be complete and balanced.

My goal is to help pet parents feel comfortable preparing food for their dogs and cats. There is no "right" way or "only" way to feed them. Pet owners have different beliefs regarding feeding raw or cooked foods; both beliefs are valid. They have different levels of cooking ability, time to prepare diets, and room to store food. Every pet is an individual and has different requirements.

By preparing your pet's food at home, diets can be modified for different disease problems and prevention. Pets should have variations in their meals, just like humans. Preparing food for your pets can cost less than buying "premium" pet foods. By purchasing and combining the ingredients yourself, you know exactly what is going into the meal. If your pet has specific protein intolerances, needs a low-fat diet, needs more fat to maintain weight, needs to lose a few pounds, or has a specific health issue, you can control the meals to address the issues at hand.

Animals with food allergies or food intolerances may need a restricted diet with novel proteins; diabetic pets need a diet low in carbohydrates; pets in kidney failure need diets with high quality, moderate protein levels that are low in phosphorous; pets with a history of oxalate stones need a low oxalate diet. Although many restricted-ingredient diets are now entering the pet food market, it may be difficult to find a product with the exact ingredients that may be needed. Some pets do not do well on any processed products, but thrive on raw or home prepared diets.

Would you ever consider pouring out a bowl of dry, complete and balanced cereal for your children twice a day with no additional food? This is downright silly, yet it is exactly what we have been taught to do for our animals.

How Much Should You Feed?

Many people struggle with math, finding this particular aspect of making pet food to be the most problematic. I've included a chart to make it a little easier for you.

Pets will consume an average of two to three percent of body weight per day, which converts to 20 to 30 calories per pound of body weight per day, depending on activity level, age, lifestyle, and breed. Larger breeds tend to need a lower percentage than smaller breeds with higher metabolism.

Dogs over 100 pounds generally need closer to 1.5% of body weight, as their metabolism tends to be slower. For instance, if your dog weighs 120 pounds, use the 2% side of the chart, adding together the amounts for 100 pounds and 20 pounds as a starting point. You may have to adjust down the amount fed if the pet is gaining weight.

For instance, a 50-pound dog eating two percent of body weight will eat approximately one pound of food per day. Our 30-pound Cocker Spaniels each eat one pound of food per day because they need closer to three percent of body weight. So, for dogs under about 40 pounds, follow the chart on the three percent side, unless they are overweight.

You should feed based on the ideal body weight, not the current body weight. Assess your pet with a critical eye at least once a week or weigh them to determine if there is too much weight gain or loss. Adjust amount fed accordingly. Your dog should have a "waist", meaning their underline tucks up behind the rib cage. You should be able to feel the ribs, not layers of fat over the ribs. Generally, people tend to keep pets too heavy. From a health standpoint, slightly underweight is healthier than slightly overweight.

RECOMMENDED FEEDING CHART

BODY WEIGHT			2% of BODY WEIGHT		3% of BODY WEIGHT	
	<5 lb	<2.3 kg	1.6 ounces	45.4 grams	2.4 ounces	68.0 grams
	5 lb	2.3 kg	1.6 ounces	45.4 grams	2.4 ounces	68.0 grams
	10 lb	4.5 kg	3.2 ounces	90.7 grams	4.8 ounces	136.1 grams
	15 lb	6.8 kg	4.8 ounces	136.1 grams	7.2 ounces	204.1 grams
	20 lb	9.0 kg	6.4 ounces	181.4 grams	9.6 ounces	272.2 grams
	25 lb	11.3 kg	8.0 ounces	226.8 grams	12.0 ounces	340.2 grams
	30 lb	13.6 kg	9.6 ounces	272.2 grams	14.4 ounces	408.2 grams
	35 lb	15.9 kg	11.2 ounces	317.5 grams	16.8 ounces	476.3 grams
	40 lb	18.1 kg	12.8 ounces	362.9 grams	19.2 ounces	544.3 grams
	45 lb	20.4 kg	14.4 ounces	408.2 grams	21.6 ounces	612.3 grams
	50 lb	22.7 kg	16.0 ounces	453.6 grams	24.0 ounces	680.4 grams
	55 lb	24.9 kg	17.6 ounces	499.0 grams	26.4 ounces	748.4 grams
	60 lb	27.2 kg	19.2 ounces	544.3 grams	28.8 ounces	816.5 grams
	65 lb	29.4 kg	20.8 ounces	589.7 grams	31.2 ounces	884.5 grams
	70 lb	31.8 kg	22.4 ounces	635.0 grams	33.6 ounces	952.5 grams
	75 lb	34.0 kg	24.0 ounces	680.4 grams	36.0 ounces	1020.6 grams
	80 lb	36.3 kg	25.6 ounces	725.7 grams	38.4 ounces	1088.6 grams
	85 lb	38.6 kg	27.2 ounces	771.1 grams	40.8 ounces	1156.7 grams
	90 lb	40.8 kg	28.8 ounces	816.5 grams	43.2 ounces	1224.7 grams
	95 lb	43.1 kg	30.4 ounces	861.8 grams	45.6 ounces	1292.7 grams
	100 lb	45.3 kg	32.0 ounces	907.2 grams	48.0 ounces	1360.8 grams

BODY CONDITION SCORE

THIN or FIT or FAT

1. VERY THIN — Very thin with ribs and pelvis prominent.

3. UNDER-WEIGHT — Below ideal weight with ribs and waist visible.

5. FIT — Good condition, can feel ribs, and has a waist.

7. OVER-WEIGHT — Above ideal weight, ribs hard to feel, no obvious waist visible.

9. VERY FAT — Very overweight with rolls of fat and large abdomen.

Obesity is rampant in pets in the United States. Statistically, over 50% of pet cats and dogs are overweight or obese. We can only blame this on pet parents who dole out too many calories. Very few pets have the ability to shop for and serve food to themselves.

I like to feed my animals twice daily, but there are some pets and owners that prefer to feed once, three, or four times daily. There are no hard and fast rules; use a schedule that works best for you and your pet. If you feed twice daily, divide the total daily requirement into two portions. For three meals, divide total daily requirement into three portions.

The recipes in this book are all based on one pound of protein as the base ingredient. After making the meal, you can then weigh out the amount of finished product needed to feed your pet. Calorie content will be different for each recipe, depending on the percent fat in the meat you use. Aim for 90% lean whenever possible; use leaner meats for pets that cannot tolerate much fat in the diet. Diets using white fish will be lower in calories; you may have to feed larger portions. By rotating diets and watching your pet's waistline, your pet should have no problem maintaining ideal weight.

Myths Debunked

Some internet sites will also list foods like garlic, mushrooms, walnuts, almonds, and liver as being toxic to pets. While garlic can cause hemolytic anemia (a much bigger problem for cats) when fed in large quantities, it also has many beneficial effects. It has antibacterial, antifungal, anti-parasitic, and antiviral properties, as well as being a good Yang tonic, transforms phlegm, drains damp, and resolves stagnation. (These properties will be discussed later.) The key is quantity fed. One clove per twenty pounds of body weight daily should be a safe level to feed. Avoid garlic if your pet suffers from hemolytic anemia, anemia in general, or a pathologic low platelet count. If you feel uncomfortable using garlic, eliminate it from the recipe.

Some mushrooms like Shiitake, Maitake, Reishi, and Turkey Tail help fight cancer, as well as draining damp. I include mushrooms in almost all my recipes. There are other mushrooms that are toxic to dogs and should be avoided. I recommend buying mushrooms from the grocery store rather than collecting your own.

Liver is high in vitamin A and is also the filtering organ for the body. Organic or grass-fed, hormone-free, antibiotic-free liver should be used. However, liver should not be fed in large quantities every day. Organs such as liver and kidney should not make up more than ten percent of the diet. Calves' liver and liver from free-range, antibiotic-free poultry will contain less toxins.

Black walnuts can cause liver damage. Black walnut is commonly used in herbal preparations for parasite prevention and treatment. Liver protectants should always be used in conjunction. Other nuts, particularly walnuts, pecans, pistachios, and Brazil nuts may be contaminated with aflatoxins from molds which can cause liver failure. The aflatoxin is usually found in the hulls, not the nut itself. Peanuts are actually legumes, not nuts, but they are also commonly contaminated with aflatoxins, and I do not recommend their use.

Cruciferous vegetables (members of the Brassica family) are very healthy and have a low-glycemic index, meaning they do not produce sugar in the body. If fed raw in large amounts they can suppress thyroid function. Since my diets are fairly low in vegetable matter, this should not be an issue. I recommend rotating meals and using varied ingredients, as well.

Vegetables are hard to digest and should be finely chopped, fermented, or gently cooked to provide absorption of nutrients. This breaks down the fibrous cell wall and releases the phytonutrients. Broccoli, cauliflower, Brussel sprouts, cabbage, arugula, Bok choy, kale, collard greens, mustard greens, turnips, watercress, rutabaga, daikon, and kohlrabi are fine to feed as described above.

Spinach and swiss chard are high in oxalates and should be avoided or only fed in small amounts if you have a pet with a history of oxalate stones or crystals in the urine. Certain small breed dogs including Yorkies, Maltese, and Bichons seem to be more susceptible to producing oxalate stones.

White potatoes, tomatoes, peppers, and eggplant belong to the nightshade family and contain a substance called solanine. Solanine may aggravate arthritis pain and other inflammatory conditions. This does not occur in all individuals who eat these vegetables, only those who are sensitive to the solanine. I generally do not include these vegetables in my recipes, other than the occasional use of red pepper which is high in vitamins A, C, thiamine, folate, and antioxidants.

TOXIC FOODS

FOODS THAT MAY BE TOXIC TO YOUR PETS

Chocolate - Contains theobromine which can cause hyperactivity, seizures, tremors, irregular heartbeat, death

Macadamia Nuts - May cause vomiting, weakness, tremors, drunken walk, death

Grapes & Raisins - May cause vomiting, diarrhea, kidney failure, death; not all dogs are susceptible

Apricot, Peach, Cherry, Plum Pits - Contains cyanide; causes vomiting, shock, cardiac arrest, death

Onions/Scallions - Causes hemolytic anemia, vomiting, diarrhea, bloody urine; effects of eating onions are cumulative

Green Tomatoes, Tomato Vines, & Leaves - Causes vomiting, diarrhea, seizure

Raw & Green Potatoes - Causes vomiting, diarrhea, seizures, heart arrhythmias

Rhubarb - Causes tremors, seizures, heart arrhythmias, kidney disease, high in oxalates

Nutmeg - Causes tremors, muscle spasms, seizures, death

Persimmon Seeds - Causes vomiting, diarrhea, fever

Raw Dough or Yeast - Produces ethanol, causes liver failure, seizures, drunken gait, coma, death

Alcohol - Causes depression, weakness, liver failure, coma, death

Raw Salmon or Trout - Can carry parasites that causes salmon poisoning. Canned, frozen, or cooked is okay.

Avocado Peel - Causes vomiting, diarrhea, fluid accumulation

Preparation and Storage

If you ask ten people what is the best food for dogs you will get ten different answers. Most people are very passionate about their beliefs in this realm. Raw feeders have differing views among themselves; some follow prey model raw which is meat, bones, organs, and no vegetation. Others believe vegetables add good nutrients. Some say dogs lack the ability to digest carbohydrates and vegetable matter, while others say they do just fine with this. Many pet owners are fearful of feeding raw and prefer to serve cooked meals.

My personal philosophy is that there is no "best" diet for all dogs. Every dog has different requirements depending on breed, age, health, and lifestyle. My own dogs eat a high-meat diet with added organs, vegetables and fruit. The only dairy I use is raw fermented goat milk. My proportions lean toward 70% meat and organ (and bones if feeding raw), with 30% vegetables and fruits. Cats are fed less vegetable matter, generally only five to seven percent of the diet.

I don't feed grains or starchy vegetables to my dogs very often, as I have found they don't digest them well. But that does not mean your dog will not do well with this addition. Some pet owners add cooked grains or starchy vegetables to decrease costs, while some pets require the addition of carbohydrates to decrease the amount of protein being fed or to maintain weight. Recipes will give the option of adding or leaving out the grain and starch portions.

I commonly use low-glycemic cruciferous vegetables which provide fiber for fermentation by the gut bacteria. This is considered a form of prebiotic, which is utilized by the bacteria in the bowel. The good bacteria in the gut produce necessary vitamins, as well as keeping harmful bacteria (Salmonella, E. coli, Clostridium) in check. The beneficial bacteria also decrease production and absorption of toxins produced by the harmful bacterial species.

Cruciferous vegetables include:

- Arugula
- Bok choy
- Broccoli
- Brussels sprouts

- Cabbage

- Kale

- Radishes

- Cauliflower

- Collard greens

- Turnips

- Watercress

Probiotics are the live bacteria themselves. Live micro-organisms live in the gut, on the skin, in the respiratory organs, and elsewhere in the body. These microorganisms make up a large part of the immune system, keeping harmful invaders at bay. These probiotics decrease inflammatory reactions throughout the body. Probiotics can be added to the diet through supplementation or feeding of fermented foods like vegetables or raw milk (cow, sheep, goat).

Fermented Vegetables (KimChi)

If you would like to make your own fermented vegetables, it's a fairly simple procedure. Warning: KimChi does have an odor.

- Make a brine using 2 teaspoons of sea salt combined with 4 cups water. Chlorinated water will impair the fermentation. Distilled or spring water is fine. Set aside.

- Grind 2 tablespoons ground fresh ginger root and 4 cloves crushed garlic together. Add to the brine of salt and water. Set aside.

- Grind the fruits and vegetables you would like to include in the mix such as red or green cabbage, carrots, apples, pears, daikon radishes, red or orange peppers, and red radishes.

- Pour the brine and herb mixture over the vegetables in a large glass jar. Seal jar loosely and allow to sit at room temperature for 4 to 5 days for fermentation to occur.

After 4 to 5 days, place the jar in the refrigerator to stop fermentation. KimChi can last up to twelve months in the refrigerator. Portions may be frozen and defrosted for use later, if desired.

Add a spoonful of the vegetable mix to meals as desired. One teaspoon per 20 pounds of body weight is generally sufficient.

Low glycemic vegetables help the body maintain steady blood glucose levels, rather than the rise and fall of blood sugar associated with diets high in starchy foods. Each time starches are fed, the pancreas has to work harder, releasing the digestive enzyme, amylase, and insulin which break down and convert the sugars into a usable form. Overfeeding of diets high in starchy foods can lead to pancreatic diseases such as insulin resistance, diabetes, and exocrine pancreatic insufficiency.

If your pet has cancer you will want to find the "cleanest" ingredients possible, sourcing grass-fed, organic, and minimally processed ingredients. The better the ingredients, the better the likely outcome. With that said, feeding whole, real food at even the most basic level will always provide better nutrition than highly processed industrialized food.

Most meats found in grocery stores tend to come from factory farming where the animals live in filthy, crowded conditions. Most are fed GMO grains. Grass-fed, grass-finished meats are preferable, but they certainly are not cheap. Factory farmed meats tend to have more bacterial contamination.

Fat content in meat is extremely variable. For most recipes, choosing beef that is 90% lean will be sufficient. Ground turkey and chicken can have extreme variations in fat content depending on the amount of skin and fat included in the grind. Again, look for 90% lean. If your pet requires a low-fat diet, leaner cuts are available.

Organ meats are an essential part of your pet's diet. Do not skip over these! Chicken and beef organs are the easiest to find. Ask your local butcher, the butcher at the local grocery, or shop ethnic markets to find these unusual ingredients. Some online sources are also available for shipping directly to your home. Freeze dried organs can be utilized in a pinch. They may be mixed with the food and rehydrated or fed as dehydrated treats.

Eggs may be lightly cooked, but the yolks should remain liquid to preserve the fatty acids found there. Raw eggs are acceptable. The egg shells may be used as a calcium supplement; this will be discussed in the chapter on supplements to balance the diet.

Avoid factory farmed fish, if possible. Choose wild caught, which can be expensive, or use small fish that are not farmed, such as sardines and mackerel. All salmon must be frozen for seven days or cooked before feeding, as it may contain a parasite that is deadly for dogs. Bones must be removed from cooked fish before feeding. Canned sardines and mackerel do not need to have bones removed, as these are soft and easy to digest. The larger the fish, the more likely it is to contain heavy metals. I don't recommend feeding large fish more than once a week.

For the hunters wanting to use wild game for pet food, rabbit and venison should be frozen for a minimum of 72 hours to kill potential parasites in the meat and organs.

Seasonal ingredients such as cranberries may need to be purchased in bulk and frozen for later use. Turkey giblets are much easier to source around the holidays. Gizzards and heart are muscle meat. If you are unable to find these ingredients you can substitute white or dark muscle meat of any protein source, although you will lose some of the benefits of the organs.

Fruits and vegetables should always be washed to remove pesticides and fungicides. Peeling skin off these ingredients can help remove much of the residue. Canned pumpkin is easy to find, but some of the nutrients have been degraded through the cooking and canning process. Fresh is always better, but it requires more work.

> The recipes contained in this book can be modified to fit the needs of your dog. Not every diet is considered 100% complete and balanced, as I feel that it is possible to achieve balance over time by providing the necessary nutrients each week. Many people will argue this belief. Personally, I like to include some meals with poultry, some with mammal meat, some with eggs, and some with fish. Do not choose one recipe and use that solely. Rotate diets. Read the chapter on supplements and balancing to learn more about balancing diets.

Some nutrients can be added with supplementation. Many of the recipes can be fed raw or can be cooked. Options will be included.

Generally, raw or lightly cooked meals are perfect for younger animals. Seniors may fare better on crock pot or partially digested foods, although many of ours have done very well fed raw diets into their mid-teen years.

When making the transition from processed to home prepared diets, each pet will react differently. If you are currently feeding kibble, it would be wise to use the recipes as a "topper" on the kibble over a period of a week or two, gradually decreasing kibble and increasing home prepared ingredients. Start with a simple recipe with a few ingredients. It is normal to see changes in the stool quality; it may soften or become harder. Probiotics, digestive enzymes, and bentonite clay can help during transition.

Meals can be prepared in small or large batches, depending on the time and storage space you have available. Portions can be stored in the refrigerator for up to five days and in the freezer for up to twelve months. Glass containers are preferred for refrigeration, with plastic containers working better for freezing. Make sure you purchase storage products rated for freezing. Freezer bags can also be used, but they are harder to stack and should not be re-used. Label the meals with freezer tape or masking tape.

Be sure to keep your utensils and preparation areas clean. Bacteria can multiply quickly on work surfaces. A small kitchen scale is a wonderful addition, but you probably won›t need it once you feel comfortable with proportions.

By making two or three batches of food, you will be able to rotate different meals with little effort. If you have plenty of time each day, freshly prepared meals are preferable.

When feeding home-prepared meals, they should not be allowed to sit out for long periods of time. Generally, this is not a problem, as most bowls are licked clean within seconds of serving.

Food should be served close to body temperature or slightly warm, as this is better for digestion and absorption of nutrients. Food should not be fed frozen or straight from the refrigerator. Warming can be achieved by sitting the container of food in a bowl of hot water, by adding some hot water to the food before serving, or gently steaming the food. (Keep in mind the Spleen, or digestive function, does not like damp, so meals should not be soupy.) Always test the temperature to make sure the food is not too hot. If you are comfortable using a microwave oven to warm food, be sure to heat the meal using a glass bowl, as chemicals from plastic containers may leach into the food.

Mix the food well after microwaving to make sure there are no hot or cold spots within the meal. Personally, I do not use the microwave to heat food for myself or my pets.

Large dogs can be served food with larger chunks of meat and bone, whereas smaller dogs may need ground meats and meals. Senior pets will generally fare better on ground diets. Vegetables should always be processed to break down the plant cell walls, releasing the phytonutrients. They may be processed by using a food processor, grinding, steaming, baking, or sautéing.

Meats, vegetables, and very small bones such as chicken wings can be ground using the grinding attachment on a kitchen stand mixer. Food processors work well for vegetables and organ meats, but not for muscle meats. If you want to grind larger bones you will need to purchase a larger grinder with a one or one and a half horsepower motor. When shopping for kitchen equipment, be sure to read reviews and watch videos showing it in use, to make sure it will perform the tasks you require.

Dried or frozen ingredients, which you might want to keep on hand because you can›t always buy fresh include:

- Organic turmeric
- Shiitake mushrooms
- Organic parsley
- Cranberries
- Organic ginger
- Organ Meats
- Puréed pumpkin, butternut squash, yellow squash, or sweet potato

Where it All Began: PUPLOAF!

When I first started researching the pet food industry I didn't like what I found. I could no longer in good conscience feed my pets processed dry kibble. I had dabbled with feeding processed raw foods, but I needed to devise a plan to change ingredients depending on the individual needs of each cat and dog. I formulated my first home-made cooked diet and named it Puploaf. Since that time, Puploaf has become known around the world and is being prepared with different ingredients to serve the needs of individuals. This diet is easily modified by adding or subtracting ingredients to treat different organ systems.

Basic Puploaf

1 pound 90% lean ground beef

4 ounces ground beef heart

3 ounces ground beef liver

8 ounces ground chicken gizzards

2 eggs with ground shell

4 ounces ground butternut squash

6 ounces ground vegetables including kale, spinach, broccoli, red pepper

3 ounces ground Shiitake mushrooms

2 ounces cranberries

1 teaspoon ground fresh ginger

1 tablespoon flax seed oil

1 teaspoon kelp or 2 ounces of mussels

2 sardines, canned in water, should be added at the time of feeding. (They can be added during cooking, but they smell bad.)

Grind and mix all ingredients together. Pour into a loaf or square baking pan or muffin pans. Bake at 325° F. for 30 to 45 minutes depending on thickness and size of pan; should be lightly done, not overcooked (juicy in the center). If you pet has a beef or chicken allergy, turkey could be substituted.

UNDERSTANDING TRADITIONAL CHINESE MEDICINE FOOD THERAPY

Yin & Yang

Traditional Chinese Veterinary Medicine (TCVM) provides information about food ingredients that allows us to design diets for nourishment as well as healing. By understanding the different properties of food, specific organs can be targeted. Diets can be changed based on personality, season of the year, age and medical conditions. The goal is to achieve balance and harmony. Without balance, disease occurs and life span is shortened. Feeding foods of varying flavors and energies according to the needs and physical constitution of the animal will result in a longer, healthier life.

Diets may need to change with the seasons in areas where there are dramatic changes in heat and moisture. Foods that are energetically warming are beneficial when the weather is cold and damp, whereas cooling food should be fed when the weather is hot and humid. Balance is the key, as shown by the Chinese symbol for Yin and Yang, where Yin is cool and moist; Yang is hot and dry.

The Chinese symbol for Yin and Yang shows a white dot within a black segment and a black dot within a white segment. The white symbolizes Yang while the black symbolizes Yin. There are equal amounts of Yin and Yang in the symbol, showing balance. The white spot within the black shows that there is always some Yang within the Yin, while the black spot within the white shows there is always some Yin within the Yang. This is apparent in the body, as all males produce some female hormones and all females produce some male hormones. It is possible to have imbalance, but it is impossible to have all Yin or all Yang.

Within the healthy body, Yin and Yang keep each other in balance. When Yin and Yang are out of balance, they cannot protect the body from invasion by pathogenic factors such as bacteria and viruses, and disease results. Balance is maintained through proper nutrition, emotional balance, and balance with the environment or external elements.

SEASONS CYCLE OF YIN & YANG

Summer
Heart &
Small Intestine
FIRE

Late Summer
Spleen &
Stomach
EARTH

Spring
Liver &
Gall Bladder
WOOD

Autumn
Lungs &
Large Intestine
METAL

Winter
Kidneys &
Urinary Bladder
WATER

CHARACTERISTICS OF YIN & YANG

YANG		YIN
Hot		Cold
Day		Night
Up		Down
Outside		Inside
Top		Bottom
Sky		Earth
Light		Heavy
Dry		Wet
Fast		Slow
Young		Old
Male		Female
Positive		Negative
Bright		Dark
Hard		Soft
Strong		Weak
Dominate		Passive
Active		Still
Large		Small
Loud		Quiet
Left		Right
Pungent/Sweet		Salty/Sour/Bitter
Red/Yellow/White		Blue/Purple/Black
Fire		Water
Tall		Short
South	(In the Northern Hemisphere)	North

Properties of Food

Every food eaten has energetic and physiological effects on the body. Sometimes that effect can be felt, like sweating after eating hot peppers; other times the changes are not noticed, but be assured they are occurring. The properties of food can be broken down into different categories. Individual ingredients may fall into more than one category, making them more versatile.

Ingredients will cool or add heat to the body, may help dissolve masses, move blood, increase energy, or encourage the production or elimination of phlegm and mucous. The way the food is grown and prepared, as well as the amount of moisture in the food, will also affect the energetics. This becomes important when choosing a diet for a specific pet.

Foods that are high in moisture and cool the body are called Yin foods or Yin tonics. Foods that are lower in moisture and add heat to the body are called Yang foods or Yang tonics. Food can also be classified by other properties that include: resolving stagnation, transforming phlegm, draining damp, blood tonics, and Qi (energy) tonics.

Yin Deficiency (too hot)

Inflammatory conditions produce heat within the body; ingredients that cool the body (Yin tonics) would be appropriate in a diet prepared for these animals. Excess heat can develop due to:

- Seasonal weather changes

- Viral or bacterial infection

- Excessive consumption of energetically hot food – dry kibble, freeze-dried food, Yang foods

- Loss of internal cooling mechanisms

- Hyperactive nature

Examples of hot conditions include:

- Acute fever or infection

- Pancreatitis

- Hepatitis

- Arthritis

- Skin infections and hot spots

- Diabetes

- Inflammatory bowel disease

- Diarrhea with blood or mucous

- Constipation

- Dry cough

- Increased thirst

- Early stages of Cushing's disease

- Aggression

- Restlessness

- Hyperactivity

Yin tonics, or cooling foods, can be added to the diet in the form of meat proteins, grains, vegetables, herbs, or fruits. Many pet owners choose to avoid grains, while others appreciate the benefits of feeding high quality grains for certain conditions. Grains should always be well cooked if being added to a home prepared diet. Vegetables should be finely ground and fed raw or fermented if the pet has too much Yang (heat).

Generally, pets that are young and energetic are considered more Yang; they are energetically hot and may need food that is somewhat cooling for them to focus on training skills. Feeding "hot" foods like lamb or chicken to a young, hyperactive Jack Russell Terrier can make the dog unbearable to live with; by calming him with cooling foods like ocean fish, the dog becomes much more tolerable and trainable.

If hot pets are continually fed hot, dry foods, the body's cooling system eventually burns out, leading to kidney failure and other diseases associated with lack of moisture. By feeding high moisture, cooling foods to the "hot" animal, the water system of the body will be spared, resulting in a longer, healthier life.

It is possible to move too far in one direction, however; the animal should be constantly evaluated and the diet should be modified as needed.

Yin tonics (cooling foods) should be fed more abundantly during hot summer weather. By adding Yin tonic foods to the diet in mid to late spring, your pet will be better prepared to deal with the heat when summer arrives.

ENERGETICS OF FOOD

MEATS & FISH:
Turkey, Duck, Cod, Clams,
Rabbit, Alligator, Shark,
Egg Whites, Mussels, Conch,
Duck Eggs, Frog, Herring,
Oysters, Scallops, White Fish,
Octopus

GRAINS & SEEDS:
Millet, Barley, Brown Rice,
Buckwheat, Chrysanthemum,
Flax Seed, Sesame Seed,
Soybean Oil, Wheat, Tofu

VEGETABLES & HERBS:
Alfalfa, Spinach, Broccoli,
Celery, Tomato, Mushroom,
Kelp, Seaweed, Cucumber,
Eggplant, Radish, Mung Bean,
Asparagus

FRUITS & NUTS:
Melons, Pear, Banana,
Strawberry, Orange, Mango,
Apple, Blueberry, Kiwi,
Persimmon, Honey

42

Basic Yin Tonic Diet

1 pound cubed or ground pork, duck, or rabbit

2 ounces turkey, beef, or chicken liver chopped or ground

4 ounces sweet potato or butternut squash chopped or processed

2 ounces spinach or kale finely chopped or processed

2 ounces asparagus finely chopped or processed

2 eggs without shell (see supplements section for use of egg shells)

Mix all ingredients together. May be served raw or baked in a loaf pan or square baking pan at 325° F. for 30 to 45 minutes or cooked in a slow cooker for 4 to 6 hours on low.

If you prefer to add grains to your pet's diet, ½ cup of cooked barley (cooling) can be added to the mix prior to baking. If making this in a slow cooker, ¼ cup dry grain can be added at the time of preparation and allowed to cook with the other ingredients.

Good Yin tonic treats include apples, pears, string beans, melons, and pieces of freeze dried or dehydrated pork, duck, or rabbit.

Yang Deficiency (too cold)

Pets that are energetically cold are Yang deficient. They need a diet that is warming (Yang tonics); ingredients that generate heat within the body will be helpful for these pets. Yang may become deficient through:

- Inactivity

- Excessive consumption of cold or raw foods

- Excessive liquid intake

- Exposure to cold weather

- Poor diet and nutrition

- Aging

- Having a weak constitution

Diseases and symptoms that may indicate a pet is too cold include:

- Chronic kidney disease

- Incontinence

- Anemia

- Generalized weakness

- Hypothyroidism in later stages

- Chronic digestive problems

Sedentary, overweight pets commonly lack the energy to get up and get going. By feeding foods that are energetically warming, Qi or energy, will be invigorated.

Yang tonics may be supplied to the diet as meat, grains, vegetables, herbs, fruits, and nuts. Again, whether you choose to use grains in your pet's diet is up to you and may depend on your pet's ability to process grains. Be sure they are well cooked if you choose to use them. Vegetables can be baked, sautéed in oil or steamed to break down the cell walls, releasing the phytonutrients for absorption.

Yang tonic (warming) foods may be fed more abundantly in the cold of winter. By adding Yang tonic foods to the diet in mid to late fall, your pet will be better prepared to deal with the cold when winter arrives. An exception to this are dogs that are constantly hot and panting, having difficulty with the heat and dry air produced inside the home when heating systems are turned on.

ENERGETICS OF FOOD

FOODS to WARM the SPLEEN

MEATS & FISH:
Venison, Lamb, Kidney, Shrimp, Lobster

HERBS:
Chives, Garlic, Dill Seed, Fennel Seed, Cinnamon, Cloves, Nutmeg, Ginger, Basil, Rosemary, Thyme, Cardamom

FRUITS:
Raspberries

46

Basic Yang Tonic Diet

1 pound chicken, venison, or lamb ground or cubed

2 ounces chicken liver chopped or ground

2 ounces chicken gizzards (substitute chicken breast meat, venison, or lamb if unavailable) chopped or ground

2 ounces chicken heart (substitute chicken thigh meat, venison, or lamb if unavailable) chopped or ground

4 ounces pumpkin chopped or processed

4 ounces broccoli chopped or processed

2 ounces red or green cabbage chopped or processed

2 ounces red pepper chopped or processed

1 clove crushed garlic

1 teaspoon grated or processed fresh ginger root

Mix all ingredients together. May be served raw or baked in a loaf pan or square baking pan at 325° F. for 30 to 45 minutes or cooked in a slow cooker for 4 to 6 hours on low.

If you prefer to add grains to your pet's diet, ½ cup of cooked oats or long grain white rice can be added to the mix prior to baking. If making this in a slow cooker, ¼ cup of dry grain can be added at the time of preparation and allowed to cook with the other ingredients.

Good Yang tonic treats include homemade ginger cookies, egg yolks, and dehydrated or freeze-dried chicken liver or chicken.

All diets must be energetically balanced, even though you may be trying to lean toward more Yin or more Yang to achieve a certain outcome. By choosing foods that are energetically neutral, it is possible to create a blend of energies. Pets that are well balanced may not need foods that are extremely cooling or warming. Foods that fall into the neutral category can be mixed with Yin or Yang tonics to balance out a meal.

ENERGETICS OF FOOD

MEATS & FISH:
Pork, Pork Kidney, Pork Liver
Quail, Wild Salmon,
Whole Chicken Eggs, Tripe,
Grass Fed Beef, Bison, Goose,
Jellyfish, Carp, Cuttlefish, Eel,
Tuna, Sardines Catfish, Squid,
Trout

GRAINS & SEEDS:
Corn, Sweet Jasmine Rice,
Beans (soy, green, string,
black, broad, kidney, red),
Black Sesame Seeds,
Green Peas

VEGETABLES & HERBS:
Peas, Yam, Cabbage, Potato,
Sweet Potato, Carrots,
Cauliflower, Radish,
Shitake Mushroom

FRUITS & NUTS:
Apples, Dates, Pineapple,
Longan, Lotus, Figs,
Lemon Lychee

Basic Neutral Diet

1 pound grass-fed beef cubed or ground

2 ounces beef liver chopped or ground

2 ounces beef heart cubed or ground

4 ounces chopped or processed sweet potato

2 ounces chopped or processed Shiitake mushrooms

2 ounces chopped or processed carrots

2 ounces chopped or processed green cabbage

Mix all ingredients together. May be served raw or baked in a loaf pan or square baking pan at 325° F. for 30 to 45 minutes or cooked in a slow cooker for 4 to 6 hours on low.

If you prefer to add grains to your pet's diet, ½ cup of cooked jasmine rice can be added to the mix prior to baking. ½ cup canned black beans could be substituted for the rice if desired. If making this in a slow cooker, ¼ cup dry grain or beans can be added at the time of preparation and allowed to cook with the other ingredients.

Good neutral treats include dehydrated sweet potatoes, freeze dried or dehydrated beef liver or heart, freeze dried green tripe, dates, and figs.

Origins of Food

It is easy to follow lists that have been generated to determine whether a food ingredient is hot, cold, or neutral, but the way the food is grown and prepared must also be taken into consideration. Meat from food animals that are raised on pasture will be cooler energetically than the meat from animals raised in confinement operations and fed grain. Most grains fed to confinement-raised animals are genetically modified, which may also influence your decision for which type of meats to purchase. Just like cows, pigs, chickens, and sheep that can be raised differently, the same factors will influence fish from the ocean. Wild caught fish will have cooler energetics than fish that are farm-raised and fed grains.

Cooler ⟶ **Warmer**

Free-range   Confinement-raised

Wild-caught   Grain-fed

Meats that are processed from the slaughter of young animals will tend to have more warming energy than meats processed from the slaughter of older animals. Grains and vegetables that are processed when they are high in moisture will be more cooling than grains and vegetables that are processed after they dry on the stalk or vine. The higher the moisture, the more cooling the food will be to the body.

How the food is prepared and served will also affect the thermal energetics of the food, with raw food at one end and dry kibble at the other end of the spectrum.

Cold ⟶ **Hot**

Raw < Canned < Freeze Dried < Kibble

When preparing meals at home for your pets, preparation methods will affect the energetics. Raw will have the coldest energetics, while grilled food will be the hottest energetically.

Raw < Fermented < Slow Cooked < Steamed < Baked < Broiled < Grilled

Energetics of Pets

Arming yourself with a list of properties associated with food ingredients is only half the battle. First you must determine whether your pet is hot or cold, has problems with dryness or too much moisture, has too much energy or a lack of energy, and what health problems need to be addressed. Remember that life is all about balance, nothing is all one way or the other. You should start by making a list in two columns: one hot and one cold. When you have finished you may find a majority of symptoms fall on one side of your list. If your pet has two equal columns, he or she is well balanced, allowing you to feed a neutral diet, adjusting for seasonality and changes that occur with age.

Your pet's breed in relation to climate can give you clues on what to feed. Alaskan or cold climate breeds like Huskies, Samoyeds, and Malamutes living in hot climates will suffer if fed warming foods. They are already too hot for the location where they live, so they will benefit greatly by being fed cooling food. Hairless breeds like the Chinese Crested or Mexican breeds like the Chihuahua need warming foods (and a few sweaters) if they live in a cold environment.

You can also get a hint by looking at what they might eat in their natural habitat. Alaskan dogs may be fed wild caught ocean fish, which are cooling in nature. Mexican dogs might be fed goat or chicken, both of which are warming foods and would be a more natural diet for them.

The amount of water your pet drinks will also tell you how to change the diet. Pets that are hot and dry or suffering with inflammatory conditions will drink a lot, while those that are cool and moist will drink very little. Many times, increased thirst will be the first indication of internal inflammation or cancer.

Thirst level will also depend on type of food being fed. Pets fed dry kibble will drink more than pets fed high-moisture diets like stew or fresh raw food. Pets that live their lives being fed dry kibble are basically in a state of constant dehydration, always trying to replace the moisture missing from their diet. Simply soaking the dry food in water does not replace the amount of moisture that was removed during the high heat processing of the food.

If your pet pants a lot, particularly at night, they may be suffering from too much internal heat. This is commonly seen in pets with endocrine diseases like Cushing's disease, hypothyroidism, or diabetes. Pets in heart failure may have rapid, shallow respiration because they have too much moisture in the lungs. It is important to determine the cause of the panting and increased respiratory rate. The normal respiratory rate for dogs is between 12 and 20 breaths per minute. Dogs with heart disease should be monitored often. Notify your veterinarian if resting respiratory rates exceed 30 breaths per minute.

Pets that suffer from excess fluid accumulation in the body, like ascites (fluid in the abdomen) from liver or heart failure, may need a diet with less moisture. They may also need foods that drain Damp. Since I never advocate feeding dry kibble, pets with excess moisture may benefit from a baked home prepared meal rather than a stew or raw food.

The environment your pet chooses will also give you clues as to whether they are hot or cold. Pets that love to be outside in the snow, seek cool tile on which to sleep, or pant a lot are too hot; they need to be fed cooling foods. Pets that love to lie outside on a sunny day, snuggle under the covers close to your body, and follow the sun's rays in the house for their napping pleasure, are animals that are cold and need to be fed warming foods.

The age of your pet will also affect the internal thermal energetics. Younger pets tend to be more energetic or Yang and have more heat in their bodies. Older pets tend to be slower and have less internal heat and energy, although this can vary depending on disease processes that may be occurring. Some older pets have used up all their cooling abilities from being fed processed dry kibble for a lifetime, so if they are hot and panting they will need Yin and Blood tonics which are cooling and moisturizing.

Pets with dry, rough foot pads, a dry, brittle coat, and a dry nose are suffering from Yin deficiency, or a lack of blood and moisture in the body. Blood is one of the major fluids in the body, providing cooling and delivery of nutrients to organ systems. These pets may also have a dry tongue that will be dark if they are hot and dry or pale if they have a blood deficiency.

When determining the energetics of your pets, remember they will not have every characteristic on one side of the list. They should have some from each side; even though they may have excess Yang, they will still have some Yin. Choose foods based on the majority of signs pointing to the condition they have.

The key to feeding is balance. Even if you decide your pet is hot, it is not desirable to feed only cooling foods. Over time it is possible to make a "hot" pet cold by feeding too many cooling foods. It is also possible to make a "cold" pet hot by feeding too many warming foods. When making a diet for your pet, choose the majority of ingredients based on the energetics you are trying to achieve, but add a few ingredients outside that energetic category to balance the meal.

DETERMINING ENERGETICS

YIN (TOO COLD)	(TOO HOT) YANG

☐ Pants Very Little   Pants A Lot ☐

☐ Sleeps Under the Covers   Sleeps on Cold Tile Floors ☐

☐ Loves to Snuggle   Does Not Like to Snuggle ☐

☐ Loves to Sleep in the Sun   Loves to Play in Snow & Cold ☐

☐ Is Sluggish   Is Very Active or Restless ☐

☐ Older Pets (Unless They   Young Pets or,
     Have a Yin Deficiency)   Old Pets with Spent Cooling ☐

☐ Black or Gray Coats   Red, White, or Yellow Coats ☐

☐ Eats High Moisture Diets   Lifelong Kibble Eaters ☐

☐ Pale, Wet Tongue   Red, Dry Tongue ☐

☐ Wet and Drippy Nose   Dry, Brittle Foot Pads & Nose ☐

☐ Drinks Very Little   Drinks Excessively ☐

Diagnosis Using Tongue Color, Coatings, and Shape

The tongue gives valuable information about the health of your pet. Observing the color, shape, size, and moisture level of the tongue allows you to determine which excesses and deficiencies are occurring. Do not try to crank open your pet's mouth to observe the tongue, as it will change size and shape when they pull it back into the oral cavity. It is best to observe when the dog is panting quietly with the tongue out, not after a rousing game of fetch! If your dog does not pant, lift the upper lip on the side of the mouth so you can examine the tongue in the area between the teeth on the side. For dogs with dark pigmentation on the tongue, find an area on the gums that is pink to make your evaluation. If you have multiple dogs, it helps to compare the differences in their tongues. Ask your friends to compare tongue colors at your next dog meet-up; soon you'll be an expert!

Tongue Colors

Normal – light red or pretty pink

Pale – light pink, indicating a deficiency of Blood or Qi, generalized weakness, or anemia

Red – bright red or redder than normal indicates heat (Yang excess or Yin deficiency) caused by inflammatory diseases, infections, or fever

Deep Red – darker than red, indicates a more severe heat problem, commonly associated with cancer, auto-immune problems, or chronic inflammation

Purple – lavender or purple color indicates stagnation, which can mean pain. May be associated with a cold or hot problem. May indicate heart problems

Pale Yellow – indicates dampness, often associated with liver or digestive problems

Bright yellow - indicates heat from infection or excess heat, often associated with liver problems

Tongue Coatings

Generally, the thicker the coating the more advanced the problem.

Normal – thin moist coating

White – indicates a cold problem. May be early respiratory infection if it is a thin coating. A thick white coating indicates a deeper damp problem with phlegm, commonly associated with digestive disorders.

Yellow – indicates a heat pattern and may be seen with infection or inflammation

Grey-Black coating – if wet this indicates a cold pattern, if dry it indicates a heat problem. Can be associated with chronic inflammatory diseases, chronic illness, and kidney failure.

Thick sticky coating – indicates accumulation of phlegm and damp, chronic gastrointestinal disorders

Excessive moisture – wet conditions including Qi or Yang deficiency, dampness, cold. May be associated with generalized weakness, edema, ascites, heart or liver failure, diarrhea.

Dry, cracked – indicates severe Yin deficiency and dryness.

Tongue Shape

Pale swollen wet tongue with thick edges – indicates Spleen Qi deficiency and signals digestive problems

Red swollen tongue – indicates a severe heat problem

Thin floppy tongue that falls out over the teeth – general Qi and/or Blood deficiency, often seen in older pets; can also be seen with Jing deficiency

Thin pale tongue with tremors – indicates extreme Qi or Blood deficiency (or both)

Tongue Regions

Tip – represents the heart and lungs; a red tip indicates heart heat

Sides – represent the liver and gallbladder

Center – represents the spleen and stomach; digestive disorders are represented in this area

Back – represents the kidneys, bladder, and intestines

TONGUE DIAGNOSTICS

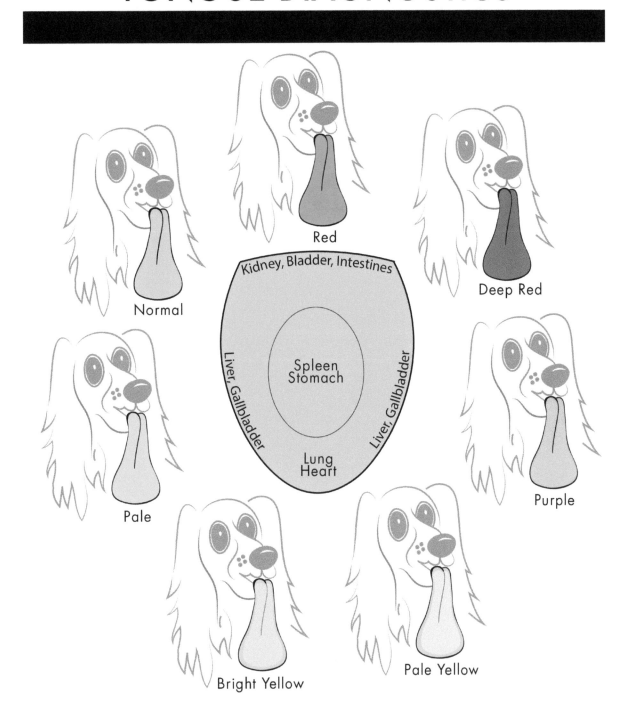

Normal

Red

Deep Red

Pale

Purple

Bright Yellow

Pale Yellow

Kidney, Bladder, Intestines

Liver, Gallbladder

Spleen
Stomach

Liver, Gallbladder

Lung
Heart

MORE PROPERTIES
OF FOOD

Qi Tonics

Qi is energy or life force. Where there is Qi, there must be life. The absence of Qi is death. It regulates spiritual, mental, emotional, and physical balance. It is impossible to have excess Qi. Since most of the Qi used in life is extracted from the food we eat and the air we breathe, Chinese medicine places considerable importance upon an adequate and appropriate diet of fresh, high quality food, and the opportunity and ability to breathe good, clean air. Feed your pets well and don't smoke around them.

The digestive system, known as the Spleen function in TCVM, transforms food into nutrients that can be used by the body. If the Spleen is not functioning correctly, food may not be properly transformed, resulting in diarrhea, weakness, and disease. The nutrients in food help produce blood, which nourishes the cells of the body; Qi moves the blood throughout the body.

Qi plays a very important role in the overall health of the animal. Qi can be damaged by:

- Environmental stresses

- Over-vaccination

- Chemical and pesticide poisoning

- Overexertion or excessive training

- Emotional stress and frustration

- Poor nutrition

- Medications

Imbalances or disruptions of the normal quantity or flow of Qi cause the body to be more susceptible to disease. Pathologic problems with Qi can include deficiency, stagnation or lack of energy flow, and rebellion in which Qi flows in the wrong direction such as vomiting.

General signs of Qi deficiency may include:

- Depression
- Exercise intolerance
- Heart disease
- Muscle atrophy
- General weakness
- Weak voice
- Anxiety or being easily frightened
- Asthma or chronic cough
- Poor appetite
- Drooling
- Diarrhea
- Weight loss
- Incontinence
- Deafness
- Chronic kidney failure
- Infertility

Qi stagnation refers to the disease process of Qi becoming blocked and thus disrupting normal Qi flow. This leads to pain, stiffness, and organ dysfunction.

- Stagnation in the liver, stomach, and large intestine are most common.
- Liver Qi stagnation will cause hyperactivity, aggression, anger, nervousness, and hypertension.
- Stomach Qi stagnation is commonly seen after over-eating and may be associated with vomiting and nausea.
- Large intestine Qi stagnation is associated with bloat, constipation, and gas.

Rebellious Qi is Qi moving in the wrong direction and includes hiccups, nausea, vomiting, coughing, and asthma.

Qi is nourished by fresh air, exercise, and good quality food. Qi is made in the body through interaction of the Spleen, Lung, and Kidney. Supporting these three organs is essential to replenish Qi. Diets that are already partially digested, such as thick stews and soups, are easier to digest and transform to replenish Qi. Raw food may still be used, but it should be ground or fermented to make digestion easier for animals with Qi deficiency.

Excellent Qi tonic herbs can be added in small quantities to any recipe, including:

✓ Sage
✓ Thyme
✓ Licorice root
✓ Cinnamon
✓ Ginger

Shiitake mushrooms are also a wonderful addition, as they help drain damp and nourish the digestive system.

ENERGETICS OF FOOD

QI TONIC FOODS

MEATS & FISH:
Rabbit, Beef, Chicken, Green Tripe, Lamb, Goat, Eel, Carp, Trout, Herring, Mackerel

GRAINS:
Millet, Corn, Oats, Long-Cooked White Rice, Brown Rice

VEGETABLES:
Pumpkin, Squash, Sweet Potatoes, Yams, Figs, Chestnuts, Lychee, Lotus Seed, Shitake Mushroom

Qi Tonic Recipe

1 pound beef, chicken, or rabbit (bone may be included if feeding raw) cubed or ground

2 ounces beef or chicken liver chopped or ground

4 ounces butternut squash, pumpkin, or sweet potato finely chopped or processed

4 ounces Shiitake mushroom finely chopped or processed

4 ounces vegetables that can include cabbage, broccoli, cauliflower, asparagus finely chopped or processed

1 teaspoon fresh thyme finely chopped

If you prefer to add grains to your pet's diet, ½ cup of cooked oats or long grain white rice can be added to the mix prior to baking. If making this in a slow cooker, ¼ cup dry grain can be added at the time of preparation and allowed to cook with the other ingredients.

Mix all ingredients together. May be served raw or baked in a loaf pan or square baking pan at 325° F. for 30 to 45 minutes or cooked in a slow cooker for 4 to 6 hours on low.

One of the most beneficial herbs for Qi deficiency, diarrhea, nausea, and vomiting is ginger. The dried herb is more warming than the fresh root, but either way it functions to warm the stomach and assist digestion. Ginger also functions to resolve stagnation, so it is perfect for animals that have overindulged. It moves blood and decreases pain and swelling associated with any kind of trauma or inflammation.

Congee is an ancient recipe that has been used for healing many ailments. Congee can be made ahead and stored in the freezer for use after an episode of illness, vomiting, or diarrhea. Different herbs, including ginger, can be added to the congee, depending on the organ system that is being healed. Congee can be fed alone as a meal replacement or mixed with other ingredients.

Congee

1 cup long grain white rice (easier to digest than brown rice due to lower fiber) or corn

1 cup diced boneless, skinless chicken breast (substitute pork or rabbit if needed)

1/8th cup grated fresh ginger root

8 cups water

Place all ingredients in a soup pot on the stove. Simmer on low for 8 to 12 hours, stirring occasionally and adding water as needed. Or, cook in a slow cooker on low for 24 hours, stirring occasionally. The longer it cooks, the more nutritious it is considered to be. When finished, the grain and meat should be fully disintegrated, leaving a nice gruel.

Congee is very easily digested and strengthens the Spleen (digestive) function.

ENERGETICS OF FOOD

JING TONIC FOODS

MEATS & FISH:
Bone Marrow, Bone Broth, Eggs, Kidney, Sardines, Anchovies, Mackerel

GRAINS, SEEDS, & NUTS:
Almonds, Black Sesame Seeds

VEGETABLES:
Kelp, Spirulina, Chlorella, Blue-Green Algae, Reishi Mushrooms, Alfalfa Sprouts, Bean Spouts

OTHER:
Bee Pollen, Raw Goat Milk, Raw Cow Milk, Vitamin D

Jing Tonics

The translation of Jing means "essence". It is the foundation of life. There are two types of Jing – prenatal, or that which we are born with, and postnatal, or acquired. Prenatal Jing determines the health of an individual at birth. It is the basis for all growth, development, and reproduction. Individuals inherit their lifetime supply of prenatal Jing from their parents. Prenatal Jing can never be in excess, but it may be deficient. Prenatal Jing is stored in the kidneys, so it is also called Kidney Jing. If a pet has problems early in life or during growth, they are due to a deficiency of the Kidney Jing.

Postnatal Jing is also called acquired Jing. This Jing comes from the food we eat and the air we breathe. We must replenish this Jing, as the Kidney Jing is in constant decline. That decline can occur more rapidly through:

- Poor diet

- Excess work

- Emotional turmoil

- Over-breeding

- Chronic disease

- Vaccination during pregnancy or in the first weeks of life

- Chronic exposure to chemicals and pesticides

Symptoms of Jing Deficiency can include:

- Stunted growth

- Breed disease predisposition such as syringomyelia in Cavalier King Charles Spaniels or hip dysplasia in large breed dogs

- Developmental orthopedic diseases

- Degenerative myelopathy

- Intervertebral disc disease

- Geriatric cognitive dysfunction

- Congenital hydrocephalus

- Infertility

- Excessive health problems in the early stage of life

- Premature aging

- Thin or gray hair

- Dental problems, loose teeth

- Generalized weakness

- Deafness

- Tongue will be small, pale or red

To treat Jing deficiency, Jing tonic foods must be added to the diet. Digestive processes need to be supported to ensure the Spleen can transform the food into high quality nutrients. The weaker the inherited essence, the more need there is to provide high quality nutrition. Chemicals and preservatives in processed food, along with genetically modified food, will weaken the essence.

Jing tonic foods are also considered to be the root of life. Seeds, which contain all the elements necessary for the growth of plants and trees, are good Jing tonics, as well as other foods that form life or come from the sea, including:

- ✓ Eggs
- ✓ Bee pollen
- ✓ Small fish from the sea
- ✓ Kelp
- ✓ Bone marrow

✓ Bone broth

✓ Almonds

✓ Microalgae (chlorella, spirulina, blue-green algae)

✓ Fermented raw goat or cow milk

✓ Kidney

✓ Reishi mushroom

✓ Vitamin D

✓ Ground sesame seeds (black sesame seeds are a better Jing tonic than white)

Bone Broth

Bone Broth is a strong rejuvenating potion high in minerals, amino acids, glucosamine, and many more valuable nutrients. The benefits of bone marrow are endless, having an influence not only over the collagen of bones, ligaments and tendons, but also DNA and RNA synthesis, and adrenal function.

From a Chinese medical perspective bone marrow broth boosts the Kidney Qi and Jing. Kidney Jing is made up of the Yin and Yang of the kidneys, with the Essence being the fundamental foundation of life.

Bone broth can be served alone or mixed with meals. It can be used for cooking grains and vegetables or re-hydrating freeze-dried food. Bone broth is a soothing liquid that can be used to nurse ill animals back to health following gastrointestinal upset or prolonged illness.

Raw bones with marrow – chicken, turkey, rabbit, beef, pork, or ox tail (I use 2 to 3 medium sized beef bones)

3 inches ginger root sliced – warming, Qi tonic, resolves stagnation

2 ounces parsley chopped – Blood tonic

4 ounces Shiitake mushrooms – drain Damp, Yin tonic

2 stalks chopped celery – cooling, drains Damp

¼ cup organic raw apple cider vinegar – helps pull the minerals and marrow from the bones

3 cloves garlic chopped (omit if your pet has a history of hemolytic anemia) - warming, drains damp, resolves stagnation, transforms phlegm

6 quarts water

Place all ingredients in a large soup pot or slow cooker. Cook on low heat for 12 to 24 hours. (12 on the stove at simmer or 24 in the crock pot on low.)

Allow to cool. Remove bones and discard. Never feed cooked bones. Strained vegetables and any meat can be added to meals. Place broth in the refrigerator and allow the fat to rise to the top. Skim fat and discard.

Bone broth can be stored in the refrigerator up to one week and frozen up to twelve months. Freezing in ice cube trays is a great way to have single servings readily available. Warm before feeding.

Feeding Jing

1 pound deboned, cooked or frozen salmon, or sardines canned or cooked

2 ounces beef kidney (eliminate if unable to source this) chopped or ground

2 ounces beef liver chopped or ground

3 eggs raw or gently cooked

4 ounces Reishi or Shiitake mushroom chopped or processed

3 ounces sprouts – bean, alfalfa, broccoli, whatever is available – chopped or processed

2 ounces kale, collards, or spinach chopped or processed

If you prefer to add grains to your pet's diet, ½ cup of cooked millet can be added to the mix.

Mix all ingredients together. Liver and kidney may be baked or sautéed in coconut oil, along with the vegetables, for a few minutes if you do not want to feed raw. Add some bone broth to give this diet extra power.

Salmon should not be fed every day. Wild caught is much preferred. Small fish may be fed more often. Lamb or young chicken can be substituted for the fish to have protein rotation.

Blood

Blood provides oxygen, nourishment and moisture to the cells and organs of the body. Blood is formed from the nutrients we eat. When blood is abundant, the pet will have plenty of stamina and good immunity. The hair will shine; tendons will be strong and flexible. It lubricates joints and allows smooth movement. Blood nourishes the mind and is the material basis for mental activity. Without good blood supply organs fail and the body dies.

Blood deficiency may be caused by:

- Chronic illness

- Stress

- Over-training

- Decreased blood production

- Blood destruction

- Blood loss

- Poor nutrition

When blood is deficient, there will be:

- General weakness

- Anxiety

- Pale mucous membranes and tongue

- Dry hair coat and dandruff

- Excessive shedding

- Dry eyes

- Decreased tear production

- Weak vision

- Poor growth of nails or cracked nails

- Tendon and ligament damage

- Less lubrication of the joints and less joint fluid

- Deterioration of the joint cartilage covering the ends of the bones

- Arthritis

- Loss of pigment from the nose, hair, and paw pads

Hidden pathogens which have not been fully resolved by the body's immune system, such as viruses, bacteria, fungi, or parasites, along with toxins that accumulate in the body, can disrupt the manufacture of blood. Excessive vaccination can result in blood deficiency.

Dogs should be wearing their best patent leather, meaning the foot pads and nose should be dark, smooth, and shiny. As dogs age, they may lose the color in their nose, which can be an indication of chronic disease with a need to step up the nutrient quality in the diet. Many times, the first evidence I see for impending heart disease in my Cavalier King Charles Spaniels is a loss of dark coloring in the nose. Loss of color indicates a Blood and Qi deficiency – there is no longer enough energy to bring the color out to the nose. If you are unsure whether your dog has lost nasal pigment, pull out those puppy photos you have stashed away. If the nose was once black and is now pink, red, or pale brown, aging and degenerative changes are occurring.

Stagnation or pooling of blood may lead to bruising, lumps or cysts, tumors, cancer, pain, heart failure, and decreased mobility. Abdominal tumors affecting the spleen and liver, such as hemangiosarcoma (a tumor of the blood vessels), are associated with blood stagnation. Blood stagnation can occur following trauma, emotional stress or frustration, and in cold weather or from eating a cold or raw diet for long periods.

Nutritional support to nourish the blood includes adequate protein intake, adequate green leafy vegetables, and a wide range of good quality foods. These foods are generally rich in iron, B vitamins, and amino acids.

- Rich red meats like beef, liver, and heart provide one of the easiest sources of blood enhancement.

- Dark leafy greens including kale, spinach, collards, and mustard greens are high in B vitamins.

- Foods that are red, orange, or dark green like sweet potatoes, yams, beets, and pumpkin support production of blood.

- Sea salt has a mineral profile very close to that of blood; a small amount sprinkled on the food can be beneficial.

- Dates, figs, beets, whole eggs, sardines, parsley, and black sesame seeds are excellent blood tonics.

- The Chinese herb dangui, which is the root of the angelica plant, is considered a powerful blood tonic.

Avoid stagnation by minimizing foods that are cold and damp. Avoid dairy products, refined grains, sugars, excess carbohydrates, and cold (in temperature) foods. Always warm food to body temperature before feeding. Stagnation can be resolved by feeding small amounts of citrus peel. Carrots are also excellent for resolving stagnation. Chamomile and dill can be added to the food. A tea of equal parts cinnamon, ginger, and tangerine peel can be made and poured over food as a simple remedy.

Blood Tonic Meal

This diet uses plenty of Blood tonics along with Qi tonics to move the blood. It can be used for anemia, pets with a pale tongue or dry skin, and pets with heart disease.

   1 pound beef cubed or ground

   2 ounces beef, turkey, or chicken liver chopped or ground

   2 ounces beef, turkey, or chicken heart cubed or ground if available

   1 large organic carrot grated or processed

   1 clove crushed organic garlic (substitute 1 teaspoon ground fresh ginger root if garlic makes you nervous)

   3 ounces parsley chopped or processed

   3 ounces kale chopped or processed

   4 ounces Shiitake mushrooms chopped or processed

   1 can sardines – may be added at the time of feeding. They stink while cooking.

If you prefer to add grains to your pet's diet, ½ cup of cooked barley (cooling) or oats (warming) can be added to the mix prior to baking. If making this in a slow cooker, ¼ cup dry grain can be added at the time of preparation and allowed to cook with the other ingredients.

Mix all ingredients together. May be served raw or baked in a loaf pan or square baking pan at 325° F. for 30 to 45 minutes or cooked in a slow cooker for 4 to 6 hours on low.

Good Blood tonic treats include hard boiled eggs, dates and figs.

ENERGETICS OF FOOD

BLOOD TONIC FOODS

MEATS & FISH:
Sardines, Whole Eggs, Beef, Liver, Heart, Bone Marrow, Pork, Oysters

GRAINS & SEEDS:
Barley, Corn, Oats, Sweet Rice, Wheat Bran, Black Sesame

VEGETABLES & HERBS:
Parsley Carrots, Kidney Beans, Adzuki Beans, Spinach, Watercress, Alfalfa Sprouts

FRUITS:
Apricots, Dates, Longan

OTHER FOODS that MAY HELP BUILD BLOOD

MEATS & FISH:
Dark Meat Chicken, Tuna, Swordfish

GRAINS, SEEDS, & NUTS:
Walnuts, Qinoa, Brown Rice, Lentils

VEGETABLES & HERBS:
Kelp, Sweet Potatoes, Yams, Beets, Pumpkin, Kale, Cabbage, Chard, Broccoli

Stagnation

When Qi and Blood do not flow freely, there is stagnation. Stagnation refers to a blockage or obstruction of the energy flow. This obstruction may be painful. A common example would be a bruise after trauma. Stagnation can occur anywhere including the body surface, muscles, joints, bones, or within the internal organs. The most common forms of Qi stagnation seen in veterinary medicine include stagnation in the joints, muscles, and liver. Generally, the tongue will be purple or lavender, but may also be dark or deep red.

Qi and Blood stagnation can occur from:

- Trauma

- Over-use

- Lack of exercise

- Over-activity of a joint or muscle

- Improper use of a joint or muscle

- Stress or emotional upset

- Lack of human interaction

- Infections

- Inflammation

- Extreme heat – forces blood out of the vessels

- Extreme cold – freezes and obstructs free flow

- Excess consumption of cold food

- Spinal misalignment

Clinical signs of Liver Qi stagnation, which are commonly seen in Wood personality animals (see the chapter on Wood personality), may include:

- Hyperactivity

- Excessive emotions

- Aggression

- Hypertension

- Nervousness

- Sensitivity on palpation along the flanks

Clinical signs of Stomach Qi stagnation, which are commonly seen in Earth animals (see the chapter on Earth personality), may include:

- Signs of stomach pain

- Vomiting

- Nausea

- Anorexia

Clinical signs of Large Intestine stagnation, which are commonly seen in Metal animals (see the chapter on Metal personality), may include:

- Constipation

- Impaction

- Gaseous colic

- Abdominal pain

Clinical signs of Bony stagnation (arthritis), which are commonly seen in Water animals (see the chapter on Water personality), may include:

- Stiffness

- Pain

- May be worse in cold

- Arthritis

- Intervertebral disc disease

- Spondylosis

- Degenerative joint disease

- Lethargy

Clinical signs of Blood stagnation, which are commonly seen in Fire animals (see the chapter on Fire personality), may include:

- Pain

- Lumps, masses, or swellings

- Breathlessness

- Dislikes massage of the affected area

- Irritability

- Tongue will be deep red or dark

Additions can be made to the diet to resolve stagnation. Most of these ingredients will be somewhat warming, resolving stagnation by increasing heat and energy. Some of these additions include:

✓ Herbs like turmeric, ginger, cinnamon, hawthorn berry, coriander, dill seed

✓ Garlic

✓ Carrots

✓ Chicken

✓ Crab (cooling)

✓ Lamb

✓ Venison

✓ Mustard greens

✓ Citrus peel

✓ Parsley

✓ Radish

✓ Watercress

✓ Vinegar

Avoid foods that are cold and damp, as this may lead to damage to the Spleen (digestion) and more stagnation. Avoid dairy products, refined sugars and carbohydrates, processed dry pet food, and cold foods.

ENERGETICS OF FOOD

FOODS to RESOLVE STAGNATION

MEATS & FISH:
Chicken, Lamb, Venison, Crab, Shrimp

VEGETABLES & HERBS:
Carrots, Radish, Watercress, Parsley, Garlic, Hawthorn Berry, Chive, Clove, Coriander, Dill Seed, Ginger, Turmeric, Vinegar

FRUITS:
Orange or Tangerine Peel,

Resolving Stagnation

1 pound chicken (hot), venison (hot), or crab (cold); (bone may be included if feeding raw) chopped or ground

8 ounces summer squash or butternut squash chopped or processed

2 ounces watercress chopped or processed

2 ounces kale, dandelion greens, or mustard greens chopped or processed

1 large organic carrot grated or processed

1 crushed clove garlic or 1 tablespoon ground fresh ginger root

If you like to feed grains, add ½ cup of cooked barley (cool) or oats (warm) before baking. If making this in a slow cooker, ¼ cup dry grain can be added at the time of preparation and allowed to cook with the other ingredients.

This diet can be ground and mixed together, cooking at 325° F. for 30 to 45 minutes in a loaf or square baking pan, cooked on low for 4 to 6 hours in a slow cooker, or fed raw.

If you have made fermented vegetables, this is the perfect time to add a tablespoon to the meal! Add at the time of feeding; do not cook them.

Good treats for resolving stagnation include carrots and radishes or homemade ginger cookies.

Dampness

Dampness is a Yin pathogenic factor that impairs Yang. It refers to the accumulation of fluids in the body. Dampness obstructs the flow of Qi, particularly in the Spleen which favors dryness and dislikes damp. Dampness is heavy and sinks, therefore fluid will accumulate in the lower portions of the body. It weighs down the body, making movements sluggish, weak, and heavy. Muscles may feel heavy, tired, or achy; joints may be painful and swollen. Symptoms will worsen in damp or humid weather.

Dampness may be caused by:

- Heavy fatty diet with excess sugars and carbohydrates

- Excess consumption of processed dry kibble

- Lack of exercise

- Overuse of drugs like antibiotics and steroids

- Overeating

- Too much moisture added to meals

- Consumption of synthetic, chemically grown food, or stale or overcooked food

- Infections

- Excess consumption of red meat

Clinical signs of dampness include:

- Edema

- Diarrhea

- Poor appetite

- Abdominal fullness

- Abdominal pain

- Stiffness

- Difficulty walking

- Weakness

- Cloudy urine

- Mucoid or bloody stool

- Oozing skin sores

- Difficulty urinating

- Prolonged, difficult to cure diseases

- Tumors

- Arthritis

- Allergies

- Animals with dampness will have a greasy white coating on the tongue

Foods that can be added to any recipe to help drain dampness include:

- ✓ Alfalfa sprouts
- ✓ Dandelion greens and dandelion root
- ✓ Radish
- ✓ Mustard greens
- ✓ Pineapple
- ✓ Pears
- ✓ Barley
- ✓ Herbs including sage, thyme, fennel, ginger, garlic, basil, fennel
- ✓ Green tea
- ✓ Pumpkin
- ✓ Millet
- ✓ Celery
- ✓ Seaweed
- ✓ Watercress
- ✓ Cranberry
- ✓ Corn silk

ENERGETICS OF FOOD

FOODS to DRAIN DAMP

MEATS & FISH:

Anchovy, Mackerel, Sardine

GRAINS:

Barley, Corn, Rye, Soybean, Buckwheat, Job's Tears

VEGETABLES:

Alfalfa, Adzuki Beans, Celery, Kidney Beans, Mung Beans,
Mushrooms, Radish, Turnip, Asparagus, Kelp, Lentil, Lettuce, Pumpkin

HERBS:

Horseradish, Marjoram, Parsley, Pepper

FRUITS:

Lemon, Cranberry, Papaya

Draining Damp

This diet can be used for any sort of swelling or edema in the legs, fluid build-up in the chest or abdomen, or when there are oozing skin sores.

  1 pound venison (hot), chicken (warm), or rabbit (cool) cubed or ground (bone may be included if feeding raw)

  4 ounces pumpkin or butternut squash chopped or processed

  2 ounces dandelion greens or mustard greens chopped or processed

  1 clove garlic crushed or 1 tablespoon grated fresh ginger root

  2 stalks celery chopped or processed

  4 ounces Shiitake, Maitake, or Reishi mushrooms chopped or processed

This diet can be ground and mixed together, cooking at 325° F. for 30 to 45 minutes in a loaf or square baking pan, cooked on low for 4 to 6 hours in a slow cooker, or fed raw.

If you like to feed grains, add ½ cup of cooked barley (cool) before baking. If making this in a slow cooker, ¼ cup dry grain can be added at the time of preparation and allowed to cook with the other ingredients.

Good treats for draining damp include pears, mushrooms, celery, radishes, and pineapple.

Phlegm

Phlegm is a thick, sticky substance produced by the body. Phlegm is formed when heat is present and moisture is lost, for example during illness when a fever is present. The heat from the body cooks the body fluids and causes them to accumulate and congeal. Think of a pot of stew simmering on the stove all day – it thickens as it cooks and moisture evaporates, leaving a thick liquid. Phlegm can also be produced when there is excess cold leading to stagnation of fluids that transform to phlegm. Phlegm is the more congealed form of Dampness.

Causes of phlegm in the body can include:

- Excess consumption of dairy products

- Fever

- Infection

- Environmental damp heat

- Excess consumption of processed dry pet food

- Excess cold causing stagnation that leads to phlegm

- Excess consumption of cold food

- Wind causing drying of fluids – may include windy days outside or dry forced air heating inside

Clinical signs of excess phlegm can include:

- Mucous discharge from the nose

- Coughing up mucous

- Asthma

- Dry eye

- Thick vaginal discharge

- Allergies

- Waxy ear discharge

- Tumors, both benign and malignant

- Obesity

- Bladder stones

- Gallbladder stones

- Kidney stones

- Pyometra

- Seizures

- Manic behavior

Treatment of phlegm requires dilution of the phlegm by adding moisture, along with Qi tonics to move the moisture through the body. The phlegm needs to be softened by warming. Foods that soften and transform phlegm will help it dissolve and move through the body. Eliminate dry kibble from the diet. Feed all meals at body temperature, never cold from the refrigerator. Feed diets that are easy to digest so the Spleen doesn't have to work so hard. Slow-cooked crock pot meals are already partially digested and make the work for the Spleen very easy. Avoid foods with added sugars or refined carbohydrates. Avoid dairy products.

Foods that can be added to any recipe to help transform phlegm include:

- ✓ Almonds
- ✓ Clams
- ✓ Pears
- ✓ Peppermint
- ✓ Apples
- ✓ Oranges
- ✓ Ginger

✓ Lemon or grapefruit peels

✓ Garlic

✓ Pepper

✓ Radish

✓ Kelp

✓ Microalgae

✓ Thyme

✓ Turnip

ENERGETICS OF FOOD

FOODS to TRANSFORM PHLEGM

MEATS & FISH:
Clams, Crab, Lobster, Shrimp, Prawn

NUTS:
Almonds, Walnuts

VEGETABLES & HERBS:
Pepper, Radish, Kelp or Seaweed, Water Chestnut, Olives, Shitake Mushrooms, Garlic, Ginger, Peppermint, Thyme, Basil, Fennel, Rosemary, Caraway, Cardamom, Marjoram

FRUITS:
Apples, Lemon or Grapefruit Peel, Orange, Pear

Transforming Phlegm

This diet can be used for dry eye, respiratory infections, and dogs with lipomas (which are form of phlegm).

> 1 pound beef (neutral to warm), chicken (warm), or rabbit (cool) cubed or ground (bone may be included if feeding raw)
>
> 4 ounces sweet potato, butternut squash or fresh pumpkin chopped or processed
>
> 2 ounces clams – if using canned clams be sure to rinse well
>
> 2 ounces turnip chopped or processed
>
> 3 ounces pear or apple chopped or processed
>
> 2 ounces asparagus chopped or processed
>
> 1 ounce daikon or red radish grated or chopped
>
> 1 teaspoon fresh thyme finely minced
>
> 1 clove garlic crushed or 1 tablespoon grated fresh ginger root

This diet can be ground and mixed together, cooking at 325° F. for 30 to 45 minutes in a loaf or square baking pan, cooked on low for 4 to 6 hours in a slow cooker, or fed raw.

For those wishing to feed grains, ½ cup of cooked barley can be added to the mix before baking or ¼ cup dry grain can be added to the slow cooker before cooking.

Pets with excess phlegm may benefit from fermented vegetables added at the time of feeding. Give 1 teaspoon per 20 pounds body weight.

Good treats for pets with excess phlegm include pears, apples, radishes, and homemade ginger cookies.

FEEDING FOR PERSONALITY

FIRE

Red coated animals are generally more Yang, with abundant energy; they fall under the Fire element. Fire types are very social and enjoy being the center of attention; they are difficult to calm down. They like to talk a lot; these animals are very vocal, barking to attract attention. Irish Setters are a good example.

The Fire element is ruled by the heart, which is closely connected with the mind, or Shen. The Heart element opens onto the tongue. Imbalances in the Heart element can lead to:

- Heart disease

- Heart failure

- Manic behavior

- Hyperactivity

- Separation anxiety

- Ulcerations on the tongue

Fire types tend to have the shortest lifespan if not supported constitutionally, as they will burn out their life flame.

Red foods nourish the heart:

✓ Tomatoes

✓ Beets

✓ Red peppers

✓ Red meats

✓ Organ meats

Heart Yin tonic foods should be added to the diet of these animals, including:

✓ Pork heart

✓ Fish

✓ Brown rice

- ✓ Spinach
- ✓ Broccoli
- ✓ Celery
- ✓ Mushrooms

Stimulants like turmeric are good in moderation; too much can stress the heart. Avoid salty and high fat foods; however, all dogs should have some salt in the diet to meet sodium and chloride requirements. Do not eliminate all salt from the diet. Like feeds like; these dogs should eat heart as part of their diet.

These animals benefit from interaction; they do not enjoy being solitary.

Heart healthy vitamins, minerals, and nutritional basics in the diet should include:

- ✓ Vitamin B1 – eggs, dark leafy greens, mushrooms, fish, and poultry
- ✓ Vitamin B6 – liver, chicken, and banana
- ✓ Vitamin B12 – lamb or beef liver, sardines, beef
- ✓ Vitamin A – liver, carrots, dark leafy greens, parsley, sweet potatoes
- ✓ Vitamin K – dark leafy greens, broccoli, eggs
- ✓ Folic Acid – liver, dark leafy greens, broccoli, asparagus, black beans
- ✓ Vitamin E – wheat germ oil, spinach, broccoli
- ✓ Taurine – heart, liver, kidney, eggs, fish, meat, unpasteurized goat milk
- ✓ Carnitine – liver, beef, pork, and heart
- ✓ CoenzymeQ10 – heart, beef, small fish
- ✓ Magnesium – kelp, spinach, black beans, barley
- ✓ Selenium – large fish, heart, barley, oats
- ✓ Omega 3 fatty acids – salmon, sardines, anchovies, krill oil

Heart Healthy Diet

1 pound beef cubed or ground

1 pound beef heart cubed or ground

3 ounces beef liver cubed or ground

2 eggs without shell (see supplements section regarding egg shells)

4 ounces carrot grated or processed

2 ounces kale finely chopped or processed

1 tablespoon fresh ginger root grated or processed

Add 2 sardines (canned) at the time of feeding.

This diet can be ground and mixed together, cooking at 325° F. for 30 to 45 minutes in a loaf or square baking pan, cooked on low for 4 to 6 hours in a slow cooker, or fed raw.

If you like to feed grains, add 1 cup of cooked brown rice (cool) before baking. If making this in a slow cooker, ½ cup dry grain can be added at the time of preparation and allowed to cook with the other ingredients.

Good treats for dogs with heart disease include pieces of freeze dried heart, green tripe, or liver, carrots, hard boiled eggs, or baked kale chips.

Raw goat milk is very high in taurine and makes a great addition, poured over the meal or served separately. Feed one ounce per 10 pounds of body weight per day.

Heart Antioxidant Diet

1 pound wild salmon, frozen for a minimum of 7 days or cooked, de-boned

8 ounces beef, chicken, or turkey heart cubed or ground

3 ounces parsley, spinach, or kale finely chopped or processed. Do not use spinach if your dog has a history of oxalate stones.

4 ounces butternut squash, pumpkin, or sweet potato finely chopped or processed

1 ounce blueberries

This diet can be ground and mixed together, cooking at 325° F. for 30 to 45 minutes in a loaf or square baking pan, cooked on low for 4 to 6 hours in a slow cooker, or fed raw (except for the salmon, unless it has been frozen for at least 7 days).

If you like to feed grains, add ½ cup of cooked brown rice (cool) or oats (warm) before baking. If making this in a slow cooker, ¼ cup dry grain can be added at the time of preparation and allowed to cook with the other ingredients.

Good treats include blueberries, Goji berries, and baked kale chips.

114

Heart Qi Tonic Diet

This diet is great for pets with breed disposition to heart disease, those with early heart disease, or those with a weakening heart.

    1 pound chicken or turkey gizzards chopped or ground

    4 ounces chicken, turkey, or beef heart chopped or ground

    2 ounces chicken, turkey, or beef liver chopped or ground

    4 ounces pumpkin, butternut squash, or sweet potato mashed, chopped, or processed

    3 ounces kale finely chopped or processed

    4 ounces Shiitake mushroom finely chopped or processed

    2 ounces fresh fennel chopped or processed

This diet can be ground and mixed together, cooking at 325° F. for 30 to 45 minutes in a loaf or square baking pan, cooked on low for 4 to 6 hours in a slow cooker, or fed raw.

If you like to feed grains, add ½ cup of cooked brown rice (cool) or oats (warm) before baking. If making this in a slow cooker, ¼ cup dry grain can be added at the time of preparation and allowed to cook with the other ingredients.

Good treats include dehydrated sweet potato, figs, sardines, dates, hard-boiled eggs, and freeze-dried tripe. Chamomile tea makes a good bedtime treat to calm the Shen (mind).

116

Draining Diet for Heart Failure

This will help move fluid if there is accumulation in the chest or abdomen. Use for dogs diagnosed with congestive heart failure or late stage liver failure.

1 pound chicken, turkey, or rabbit cubed or ground (bone may be included if feeding raw)

½ pound chicken or turkey gizzards chopped or ground

4 ounces mix of mustard greens, cabbage, broccoli, turnip chopped or processed

2 ounces fresh basil chopped or ground

4 ounces Shiitake mushrooms chopped or ground

2 stalks celery chopped or ground

Add 2 canned sardines at the time of serving.

This diet can be ground and mixed together, cooking at 325° F. for 30 to 45 minutes in a loaf or square baking pan, cooked on low for 4 to 6 hours in a slow cooker, or fed raw.

If you like to feed grains, add ½ cup of cooked barley before baking. If making this in a slow cooker, ¼ cup dry grain can be added at the time of preparation and allowed to cook with the other ingredients.

Good treats include celery, radishes, and carrots. Chamomile tea can also be served alone or mixed with meals.

EARTH

Yellow or tan coated dogs are generally Earth animals, tending toward obesity and a friendly, mellow attitude. An example would be a yellow Labrador Retriever.

Earth is ruled by digestion. Digestion feeds the muscles, which support the body. Imbalances will predispose these animals to:

- Digestive disorders

- Anorexia

- Vomiting

- Diarrhea

- Constipation

- Obesity

- Muscle atrophy

- Weakness of the limbs

- Edema

- Chronic hemorrhage

Dampness is the enemy of the Earth and digestion. Warming, drying herbs can be added to any diet to nurture this element:

✓ Cinnamon

✓ Garlic

✓ Ginger

✓ Turmeric

Yellow foods feed this element. Recommended foods include:

- ✓ Green tripe
- ✓ Lamb
- ✓ Chicken
- ✓ Pumpkin
- ✓ Sweet potato
- ✓ Corn – non-GMO!

Avoid processed foods. Like feeds like; these animals should have rumen (green tripe) and spleen included in their diet.

These animals benefit from massage and muscle strengthening exercises.

Earth Diet

1 pound chicken or lamb cubed or ground (bone may be included if feeding raw)

8 ounces sweet potato, butternut squash, or fresh pumpkin cubed or processed

4 ounces dark leafy greens chopped or processed – kale, spinach, collards, mustard or dandelion greens

2 ounces Shiitake, Maitake, or Reishi mushrooms chopped or processed

1 teaspoon ground dried cinnamon or dried ginger

This diet can be ground and mixed together, cooking at 325° F. for 30 to 45 minutes in a loaf or square baking pan, cooked on low for 4 to 6 hours in a slow cooker, or fed raw.

If you like to feed grains, add ½ cup of cooked corn (neutral) or oats (warm) before baking. If making this in a slow cooker, ¼ cup dry grain can be added at the time of preparation and allowed to cook with the other ingredients.

If feeding raw, fresh green tripe could be used as the protein source instead of chicken or lamb.

Beneficial treats include freeze dried green tripe and homemade ginger cookies.

Treating Diarrhea

Two forms of diarrhea are possible.

Bland Diet for Cold Diarrhea

Cold diarrhea is commonly seen in weak or geriatric pets. The diarrhea has minimal odor, may be gray or light tan in color, and may contain undigested food. A warming diet is needed for treatment. Congee made with chicken and white rice works well to get pets eating if they have lost their appetite.

1 pound low-fat ground chicken or venison baked, boiled, or sautéed.

1 teaspoon ground dried cinnamon or ground dried ginger

12 ounces well-cooked mashed butternut squash or pumpkin

4 ounces Portobello mushroom chopped or processed

If you like to feed grains, ½ cup of well-cooked long grain white rice can be added.

Mix all ingredients. Feed small quantities multiple times per day until normal stool is observed.

Bland Diet for Hot Diarrhea

Hot diarrhea can be seen with bacterial or viral infections, colitis, and inflammatory bowel disease. This stool will have a very foul odor and may contain blood or mucous. A cooling diet is needed for treatment. Congee made with rabbit or pork and barley works well to get pets eating if they have lost their appetite.

1 pound low-fat ground turkey, pork, or rabbit baked, boiled, or sautéed

1 teaspoon ground fresh ginger root

12 ounces well-cooked mashed apple or sweet potato

4 ounces Portobello mushroom chopped or processed

If you like to feed grains, ½ cup of well-cooked millet or barley can be added.

Mix all ingredients. Feed small quantities multiple times per day until normal stool is observed.

Supplements which may be beneficial for digestive health include:

✓ Probiotics

✓ Prebiotics – FOS, fiber

✓ Digestive enzymes – amylase, lipase, pepsin, pancreatin, papain (papaya), bromelain (pineapple)

There are many suppliers of these supplements that can be added to the diet. However, these ingredients can also be found in whole food such as kefir, raw fermented goat milk, KimChi, tripe, papaya, and fresh pineapple. Avoid commercial products with additives or base mixes such as animal digest or meat and bone meal, as these come from rendered animals that may have been unhealthy prior to slaughter.

The Pancreas

The pancreas plays an important role in the process of digestion; it falls under the Earth element. Pancreatitis is a common inflammatory disease; it can be acute or chronic. Pancreatitis can be caused by:

- Chronic inflammation
- Medications including steroids
- Chronic diseases such as Cushing's disease
- Diets high in chemicals and rancid fats
- Diets high in processed fats
- Deficiencies of antioxidants
- Breed disposition (Yorkies, miniature Schnauzer)
- Pesticides
- Excess cold causing obstruction of Qi and Blood flow
- Prolonged emotional upset or frustration
- Overindulgence in food resulting in food stagnation and generation of heat

As you can see, there are many causes other than high fat diets. I often see patients that have had no changes in their diet, yet they have acute pancreatitis. Stress and other factors play a major role in this disease. I commonly have clients asking how to eliminate fats from their pet's diet. This is not desirable or wise! Fats are an important part of the diet. Fat soluble vitamins A, D, E, and K are stored in the fat and released as needed. These vitamins are critical for eye, bone, skin, coat, and immune system health, as well as maintaining the ability to make clotting factors for blood. Dogs on low fat diets for extended periods of time will have dull, dry coats and flaky skin. Extremely low-fat diets can lead to insulin resistance, eye disease, and cognitive dysfunction.

Symptoms of pancreatitis may include:

- Vomiting
- Diarrhea that may be bloody

- Anorexia

- Lethargy

- Abdominal pain

- Dehydration

- Licking the air

- Irritability

Supplements and ingredients recommended for pets with pancreatitis:

✓ Antioxidants – N-Acetyl Cysteine, CoQ10, Vitamin E

✓ Vitamin B12 and folic acid

✓ Herbs including ginger, peppermint, chamomile, turmeric

✓ Citrus peel

✓ Dandelion greens

✓ Dark leafy greens

✓ Pancreas – like treats like

✓ Foods high in carotene and lycopene – orange and red foods – red, orange, or yellow peppers

✓ carrots

✓ Medium chain triglycerides – coconut oil

✓ Digestive enzymes – fresh papaya, fresh pineapple, animal-based enzymes, green tripe

Avoid heavily processed foods cooked at high heats. Avoid rancid fats by feeding fresh food. Some pets will have difficulty tolerating fish oils added to the diet. Medium chain triglycerides, such as high-quality coconut oil will generally be well tolerated and can be used to provide some fat in the diet. Yellow foods are good for treatment. Feed small meals often; avoid large meals. Avoid hot foods and vinegar. Congee is a good meal to provide after a bout of acute pancreatitis.

Pancreatitis Diet

This diet would also work well for diabetes and Cushing's disease. Butternut squash or pumpkin would be a better choice than sweet potato for diabetic pets.

1 pound boneless, skinless chicken or turkey breast or rabbit cubed or ground

6 ounces chicken or turkey gizzards chopped or ground

3 ounces chicken or calves' liver chopped or processed

2 ounces beef pancreas if available

1 tablespoon fresh ginger root chopped or processed

4 ounces butternut squash, pumpkin, or sweet potato finely chopped or ground

3 ounces kale finely chopped or ground

4 ounces Shiitake mushrooms finely chopped or ground

2 ounces asparagus finely chopped or ground

This diet can be ground and mixed together, cooking at 325° F. for 30 to 45 minutes in a loaf or square baking pan, cooked on low for 4 to 6 hours in a slow cooker, or fed raw. Many pets with pancreatitis will do better when the food is partially digested, so the slow cooker stew may work best.

If you like to feed grains, add ½ cup of cooked barley before baking. If making this in a slow cooker, ¼ cup dry grain can be added at the time of preparation and allowed to cook with the other ingredients.

These pets may benefit from the addition of fermented vegetables at one teaspoon per 15 pounds body weight per meal.

Raw goat milk contains abundant probiotics and enzymes and can be very beneficial for these pets. It is low in fat (averaging 3%). It can be served alone or served with meals.

Pancreatitis Diet Take Two

This diet would also work well for diabetes and Cushing's disease. Butternut squash or pumpkin would be a better choice than sweet potato for diabetic pets.

1 pound white fish (cod, halibut, tilapia, flounder, mackerel, sardine) baked, boneless

2 ounces beef pancreas if available, raw or gently sautéed in coconut oil

4 ounces chopped broccoli, steamed

4 ounces mashed cooked butternut squash, sweet potato, or pumpkin

1 teaspoon coconut oil

1 teaspoon fresh ginger root grated or processed

Mix all ingredients together and serve.

Good treats include freeze dried green tripe.

These pets may benefit from the addition of fermented vegetables at one teaspoon per 15 pounds body weight per meal.

Raw goat milk contains abundant probiotics and enzymes and can be very beneficial for these pets. It is low in fat (averaging 3%). It can be served alone or served with meals.

Pancreatitis Diet Take Three

This diet would also work well for diabetic pets and dogs with Cushing's disease. Butternut squash or pumpkin would be a better choice than sweet potato for diabetic pets.

1 pound skinless turkey cubed or ground (can include bone if feeding raw)

2 ounces chicken or turkey liver chopped or processed

2 ounces beef pancreas if available

4 ounces butternut squash, sweet potato, or pumpkin chopped or processed

4 ounces yellow squash chopped or processed

2 ounces turnip chopped or processed

2 ounces parsley chopped or processed

Add 2 canned sardines in water at the time of feeding.

This diet can be ground and mixed together, cooking at 325° F. for 30 to 45 minutes in a loaf or square baking pan, cooked on low for 4 to 6 hours in a slow cooker, or fed raw. Many pets with pancreatitis will do better when the food is partially digested, so the crock pot stew may work best.

If you like to feed grains, add ½ cup of cooked barley before baking. If making this in a slow cooker, ¼ cup dry grain can be added at the time of preparation and allowed to cook with the other ingredients.

Good treats include hard-boiled egg white or whole eggs, freeze dried green tripe, or home made ginger cookies.

Obesity

Over 50% of the dogs and cats in the United States are overweight or obese. Earth animals tend toward obesity, slower metabolism, and generally laid-back attitudes. Obesity has many causes including:

- Overfeeding
- Lack of exercise
- Breed predisposition
- Improper diet
- Endocrine diseases like hypothyroidism and Cushing's disease

If your pet is overweight you must see your veterinarian to have blood drawn. Have your pet tested for diabetes, thyroid dysfunction, and Cushing's disease. If any of these are diagnosed, the disease must be treated. Along with treatment for the disease, diet should be changed to support weight loss and decrease inflammation in the body.

Obesity can predispose pets to additional problems including:

- Chronic inflammation
- Joint disorders
- Heart disease
- Metabolic disease
- Endocrine disease
- Skin infections
- Kidney dysfunction
- Cancer
- Reduced life expectancy

Ingredients that may promote weight loss include:

- ✓ Barley
- ✓ Cruciferous low glycemic veggies
- ✓ Moderate fat

Supplements to enhance weight loss include:

- ✓ Vitamin C - prevents accumulation of fat in liver cells; citrus fruits may be used
- ✓ Garlic - resolves stagnation, blocks intestinal cholesterol absorption
- ✓ Ginger - antioxidant, appetite suppressant, aids digestion, Qi tonic to increase metabolism
- ✓ Turmeric - Qi tonic for metabolism, fights inflammation associated with obesity
- ✓ Omega 3 fatty acids - decrease triglycerides
- ✓ Spirulina or chlorella – rich in vitamins E and C, B vitamins, copper, zinc, manganese, and fiber; aids digestion, metabolism, removing toxins, and preventing fat absorption.

Avoid processed foods high in carbohydrates and fats. Feed small meals more frequently rather than fewer large meals. Snacks must be very low calorie and limited. Fresh fruits and vegetables make excellent snacks, including blueberries, green beans, watermelon, coconut, and broccoli.

Weight Loss Diet

This diet would work well for pets with diabetes and Cushing's disease. Grains are not recommended for diabetics to maintain more even blood sugar levels; however, barley is a low-glycemic grain.

1 pound lean turkey, chicken, or rabbit cubed or ground (bones may be included if feeding raw)

3 ounces turkey, chicken or rabbit liver chopped or processed

2 ounces kale, spinach, or collards finely chopped or processed

2 ounces red or green cabbage, broccoli, or cauliflower finely chopped or processed

2 stalks celery finely chopped or ground

1 egg without shell (see supplement section for use of egg shells)

1 tablespoon fresh ginger root grated or ground

This diet can be ground and mixed together, cooking at 325° F. for 30 to 45 minutes in a loaf or square baking pan, cooked on low for 4 to 6 hours in a slow cooker, or fed raw.

If you like to feed grains, add ½ cup of cooked barley before baking. If making this in a slow cooker, ¼ cup dry grain can be added at the time of preparation and allowed to cook with the other ingredients.

Weight Loss Diet Take Two

This diet would work well for pets with diabetes and Cushing's disease. Diabetic pets generally maintain more even blood sugar levels if they are not fed grains. Barley is cooling, draining, and has low glycemic value; if you must feed grains it would be the best choice.

1 pound white fish (tilapia, sardine, cod, mackerel, anchovy, flounder) baked and de-boned (unless using canned)

2 ounces chicken, turkey, or beef liver raw, baked, or sautéed

8 ounces raw green veggies or salad greens chopped or processed

1 egg raw or gently cooked leaving yolk runny

1 tablespoon coconut oil

1 teaspoon fresh ginger root grated or processed

If you like to serve grains, add ½ cup of well-cooked barley.

Mix all ingredients together. Serve.

WATER

Black or gray coated animals tend to have a Water constitution, which is generally more Yin, tending to be somewhat fearful, running away and hiding when confronted. They will bite in fear if they are unable to flee. These animals tend to stand back and observe, analyzing the world around them. They prefer warm environments and are intolerant to cold. The Weimaraner is a good example of this element.

This element is ruled by the kidneys. Kidneys control reproduction, the bones and teeth, and the nervous system. Imbalances in the water element can lead to:

- Infertility
- Arthritis
- Seizures
- Bladder cancer
- Kidney disease
- Developmental growth disorders
- Fear
- Adrenal fatigue
- Dental disease

Black or dark foods and salty foods feed this element. Ingredients that feed the water element include:

✓ Kidney

✓ Eggs

✓ Duck

✓ Green tripe

✓ Sardines

✓ Mussels

✓ Oats

✓ Sweet potato

✓ Black sesame seeds

✓ Black beans

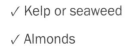

✓ Kelp or seaweed

✓ Almonds

Warming herbs that can be added to any diet for this element include:

✓ Ginger

✓ Cinnamon

✓ Garlic

✓ Turmeric

Like feeds like; these animals should have some kidney and bone broth included in their diet. Jing tonics are useful for these animals. These animals benefit from chiropractic care and maintaining a supple spine.

144

Kidney Support Diet

1 pound chicken chopped or ground (bones may be included if feeding raw)

4 ounces beef, lamb, or pork kidney chopped or ground, rinse well before using to decrease odor

4 ounces pumpkin, sweet potato, or butternut squash chopped or processed

2 ounces parsley or kale finely chopped or processed

2 eggs without shell (see supplement section regarding use of egg shells)

4 ounces Maitake or Shiitake mushroom chopped or processed

1 teaspoon ground cinnamon

1 tablespoon sesame oil

This diet can be ground and mixed together, cooking at 325° F. for 30 to 45 minutes in a loaf or square baking pan, cooked on low for 4 to 6 hours in a slow cooker, or fed raw. Kidney does smell a bit like urine when cooking.

If you like to feed grains, add ½ cup of cooked millet or quinoa before baking. If making this in a slow cooker, ¼ cup dry grain can be added at the time of preparation and allowed to cook with the other ingredients.

Supplement with spirulina, chlorella, or blue-green algae. Raw goat milk and bone broth are very beneficial for kidney support.

Good treats include figs, dates, sardines, green tripe, and almonds.

Kidney Support Diet Take Two

This diet would work well for diabetic dogs. Do not add grains for diabetics.

> 1 pound wild caught salmon or white fish (cod, tilapia, flounder, sardine, anchovy, mackerel) cooked and de-boned
>
> 4 ounces butternut squash, pumpkin, or sweet potato finely chopped or processed
>
> 3 ounces mixed kale, asparagus, and cabbage finely chopped or processed
>
> 4 ounces white mushrooms chopped or processed
>
> 1 egg without shell (see supplement section regarding use of egg shells)
>
> 1 tablespoon fresh basil finely chopped or processed
>
> 1 teaspoon sesame seed oil
>
> 1 teaspoon coconut oil

Fish may be baked or sautéed. Vegetables and herbs may be steamed, sautéed in oils, or fed raw if finely ground. Egg may be fed raw or cooked.

If you like to feed grains, add ½ cup of cooked millet or quinoa before feeding.

Supplement with spirulina, chlorella, or blue-green algae. Raw goat milk and bone broth are very beneficial for kidney support.

Kidney Yin Deficiency Diet

These pets will be drinking excessively, have dry coat and nose, and a dry tongue. This is an excellent diet for diabetic dogs. Do not add grains for diabetics; squash or pumpkin would be better than sweet potato for diabetics.

> 1 pound duck, pork, beef, or quail cubed or ground (include bones if feeding raw)
>
> 6 ounces beef or pork kidney cubed or ground
>
> 2 ounces clams rinsed well
>
> 4 ounces sweet potato, butternut squash, or pumpkin chopped or processed
>
> 4 ounces mixed vegetables including red or green cabbage, asparagus, and carrots ground or processed
>
> 1 apple chopped or processed
>
> 1 egg without shell (see supplement section regarding use of egg shells)
>
> 1 teaspoon sesame oil

This diet can be ground and mixed together, cooking at 325° F. for 30 to 45 minutes in a loaf or square baking pan, cooked on low for 4 to 6 hours in a slow cooker, or fed raw.

If you like to feed grains, add ½ cup of cooked barley, millet, or quinoa before baking. If making this in a slow cooker, ¼ cup dry grain can be added at the time of preparation and allowed to cook with the other ingredients.

Supplement with spirulina, chlorella, or blue-green algae. Raw goat milk and bone broth are very beneficial for kidney support.

Good treats include coconut milk, apple, carrots, freeze-dried tripe. Diabetic pets do well with freeze-dried tripe, green beans, broccoli, or banana as treats.

Raw goat milk is cooling and is a complete diet; it may be fed as a stand-alone meal for these pets.

Kidney Yang Diet

These pets may be old and cold, seeking warmth. They may be weak and have no appetite in the morning.

1 pound chicken or venison cubed or ground

4 ounces beef or lamb kidney

6 ounces sweet potato finely chopped or processed

2 ounces radicchio, leaf chicory, red cabbage, or watercress finely chopped or processed

3 ounces broccoli chopped or processed

1 egg without shell (see supplement section regarding use of egg shells)

1 teaspoon ground cinnamon or ginger

1 tablespoon coconut oil

This diet can be ground and mixed together, cooking at 325° F. for 30 to 45 minutes in a loaf or square baking pan, cooked on low for 4 to 6 hours in a slow cooker, or fed raw.

If you like to feed grains, add ½ cup of cooked oats or quinoa before baking. If making this in a slow cooker, ¼ cup dry grain can be added at the time of preparation and allowed to cook with the other ingredients.

Supplement with spirulina, chlorella, or blue-green algae. Raw goat milk and bone broth are very beneficial for kidney support.

Good treats include home-made ginger cookies.

Breakfast for Kidney Yang Deficiency

This is a warm breakfast made with warming (Yang) ingredients. It is very useful for cold pets or seniors, as well as being beneficial on cold days.

½ cup cooked oatmeal

½ teaspoon ground cinnamon

1 scrambled egg

Mix all together. Oatmeal can be cooked in bone broth or fish broth to encourage eating. Meal should be fed warm, releasing the odors.

Additions to the diet that would be beneficial, include pumpkin, ginger, sardines, apples, cranberries, coconut oil, raw goat milk or kefir, or banana. Choose ingredients your pet loves.

Bladder Damp Heat Diet

This diet is useful for pets prone to repeated bladder infections or stone formation.

1 pound beef or duck chopped or ground (may include bone if feeding raw)

3 ounces beef or duck liver chopped or ground

2 ounces crab

2 ounces clam rinsed well

4 ounces sweet potato finely ground or processed

8 ounces mixture of cabbage, asparagus, celery, and carrot finely ground or processed

¼ cup cranberries ground or chopped

1 tablespoon lemon juice

This diet can be ground and mixed together, cooking at 325° F. for 30 to 45 minutes in a loaf or square baking pan, cooked on low for 4 to 6 hours in a slow cooker, or fed raw.

If you like to feed grains, add ½ cup of cooked barley before baking. If making this in a slow cooker, ¼ cup dry grain can be added at the time of preparation and allowed to cook with the other ingredients.

Supplement with glucosamine for bladder support.

Good treats include watermelon, cantaloupe, hard-boiled eggs, and freeze-dried chicken or venison.

OXALATES in FOOD

LOW OXALATES:
Beef, Chicken, Turkey, Lamb, Liver (all), Organ Meats (all), Clams, Cod, White Fish, Oysters, Salmon, Tuna, Butter, Cottage Cheese, Eggs, Goat Milk, Vegetable Oils, Oat bran, White Rice, Apples, Pears, Watermelon, Cranberries, Coconut, Banana, Apricot, Lemon, Pineapple, String Beans, Asparagus, Broccoli, Brussels Sprouts, Cabbage, Cauliflower, Cucumber, Parsley, Peppermint, Sage, Thyme, Ginger, Garlic, Basil, Dill, Lettuce, Mushrooms, Peppers, Pumpkin Squash

MODERATE OXALATES:
Walnuts, Black Pepper, Cloves, Pasta, Oatmeal, Tofu, Brown Rice, Rye Flower, Blueberries, Lemon Peel, Mandarin Oranges, Mango, Orange & Peel, Prunes, Kidney Beans, Pinto Beans, Carrots, Celery, Adzuki Beans, White Potatoes, Summer Squash, Tomatoes, Winter Squash

HIGH OXALATES:
Peanuts, Lentils, Turmeric, Soy Milk, Soybeans, Barley, Cornmeal, Wheat Flour, Rice Flour, Whole-wheat Pasta, Wheat Bran, Apricots, Figs, Okra, Collard Greens, Mustard Greens, Sweet Potatoes, Black Beans, White Beans, Chili Beans, Navy Beans, Pink Beans

VERY HIGH OXALATES to AVOID:
Almonds, Buckwheat, Beets, Sesame Seeds, Spinach, Swiss Chard

Bladder Stones

There are many forms of bladder stones that may be found in dogs; the two most common are struvite and oxalate.

Struvite stones form in urine with a high pH and occur secondary to bacterial infections. Grain-based diets tend to cause a higher urine pH than meat-based diets. Elimination of infections will prevent future stone formation. Cranberries contain natural substances that decrease the ability of E. coli bacteria to stick to the bladder wall; these are a good addition to the diet of dogs prone to urinary tract infections. Frequent monitoring of urine pH will help keep these pets stone-free. High moisture diets, such as home prepared meals instead of kibble, will help keep urine flowing, decreasing stagnation in the bladder.

Oxalate stones form in urine with a lower pH and tend to be more diet-related than struvite stones. Bacterial infections often occur secondarily to the stone formation. Kidney stones are almost always oxalate stones. Certain breeds are more prone to oxalate stone formation, including Maltese, Yorkies, Schnauzers, Shih Tzu, and Bichons. Diets should be formulated with ingredients that are lower in oxalate content.

Kidney Failure Diet

Tripe has the best calcium:phophorous ratio as a protein source for kidney failure. This diet smells awful, but most dogs love it.

1 pound green tripe raw, chopped

½ pound beef, pork, or lamb kidney rinsed, chopped or ground, raw or lightly cooked

4 ounces beef, pork, or lamb lung chopped or ground, raw or lightly cooked

8 ounces butternut squash, pumpkin, or sweet potato cooked and mashed

4 ounces asparagus finely chopped or processed

4 ounces Shiitake mushrooms chopped or processed

3 egg yolks raw

2 sardines canned in water

Mix all ingredients as listed.

If you like to feed grains, add ½ cup of cooked barley, millet, or white rice. Tip: grains will be lower in phosphorous if toasted before cooking. This is only important for pets with kidney disease and is not a necessary step when using grains in other diets.

Tips for Dogs with No Appetite

Keep freeze-dried tripe on hand. Very often they will eat that when nothing else works. Crush and sprinkle on meals to entice picky pups. It can be stored in the freezer.

Green tripe can be fed raw or cooked in the crock pot. Warning: tripe has a very foul odor! This odor may linger in your home. Cooking outside may be preferred.

Omelet for Kidney Disease

6 ounces tripe chopped fine

2 eggs beaten

1 tablespoon bone marrow

Mix together and feed raw or gently cook on the stove top. Warning: Tripe smells bad when cooked! Odor may linger in your home!

If you would prefer to make it into a casserole, add a little almond flour and water, mix and bake at 325 for 20 minutes or until firm.

Can be served with cooked kidney beans, black beans, pasta, rice, or organic tofu. The beans, pasta, and rice will be more beneficial if cooked in bone broth or fish stock.

Tripe Gelatin

After gently cooking tripe on the stove-top (Warning: foul odor!), remove the solids leaving the drippings in the pan. Mix in a tablespoon of almond flour. It will thicken and become tripe gelatin. If you don't have flour, don't worry; it will still make gelatin without the flour when placed in the refrigerator. When re-heated, this makes a nice tripe gravy that even the most finicky pets can't resist.

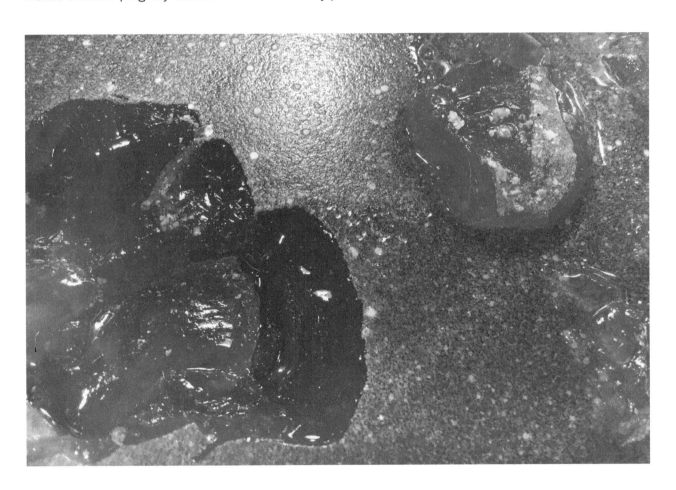

Tripe Meat Balls

Mold tripe, egg, and almond flour into a ball. Sauté in coconut oil or butter on the stove top. (Warning! Foul odor!) These can be hand-fed when your dog doesn't want to eat. The drippings can be used for Tripe Gelatin.

Pets in kidney failure and pets with cancer will have days when they just have no appetite. There are a few ingredients that should be kept on hand to pull out in a pinch.

First Aid in the Freezer

- Raw goat milk
- Fermented fish stock
- Bone broth - beef
- Bone broth – chicken
- Green tripe
- Congee
- Cooked, puréed rabbit with yellow squash

Additions to Keep on Hand

- Wild canned sardines in water

- Freeze-dried green tripe

- Freeze-dried lung

- Almond butter

Bones are controlled by the Water element. The Water element must be supported for pets with arthritis, joint disease, or developmental bone disorders.

Dietary supplement ingredients to support bone health include:

✓ New Zealand deer antler velvet – stimulates regeneration of cells

✓ New Zealand green lipped mussels – excellent source of trace minerals

✓ Glucosamine, chondroitin, hyaluronic acid – cartilage, green lipped mussels, deer velvet are natural sources

✓ Vitamin C – citrus, lettuce

✓ Manganese - kelp, spirulina, chlorella, mussels

✓ Vitamin E – almonds, spinach, sweet potato, sunflower seeds

✓ Omega 3 fatty acids – sardine, anchovy, salmon, fish oils, and krill oil

Bone Support Diet

1 pound wild caught salmon with skin, de-boned

1 cup bone broth

8 ounces fresh pumpkin or butternut squash diced

4 ounces fresh beets diced

1 tablespoon parsley chopped

1 tablespoon fresh ginger grated or finely chopped

1 stalk celery finely chopped

Simmer pumpkin or squash, along with beets, celery and herbs, in bone broth until soft. Add salmon and simmer until cooked through.

Warming Diet for Arthritis Worse in Winter

1 pound chicken or lamb chopped or ground (can include bone if feeding raw)

6 ounces sweet potato cooked and mashed

3 ounces kale chopped or processed, may be steamed or gently sautéed in coconut oil

2 teaspoons fresh ginger root grated or processed

Top with 2 sardines at the time of feeding.

This diet can be ground and mixed together, cooking at 325° F. for 30 to 45 minutes in a loaf or square baking pan, cooked on low for 4 to 6 hours in a slow cooker, or fed raw.

If you want to feed grains, add ½ cup of cooked buckwheat, brown or white rice, or oats before baking. If using the slow cooker, ¼ cup dry grain can be added and allowed to cook with the other ingredients.

Cooling Diet for Arthritis Worse in Summer

1 pound grass-fed beef, turkey, rabbit, or pork chopped or ground (can include bone if feeding raw)

6 ounces mixed salad greens, cucumber, spinach, kale chopped or processed

4 ounces yellow squash chopped or processed

2 carrots grated or processed

1 egg without shell (see supplement section for use of egg shells)

Top with 2 sardines at the time of feeding.

This diet can be ground and mixed together, cooking at 325° F. for 30 to 45 minutes in a loaf or square baking pan, cooked on low for 4 to 6 hours in a slow cooker, or fed raw.

If you want to feed grains, add ½ cup of cooked barley or brown rice. If using the slow cooker, add ¼ cup dry grain before cooking, allowing grain to cook with the other ingredients.

WOOD

Brown coated and multi-colored dogs are often found in the Wood element. They are generally more Yang in nature and tend to be dominant; they lash out when things are not going their way, biting without much provocation. These dogs are confident and competitive, making great hunters or agility dogs. Border Collies and Chesapeake Bay Retrievers are an example of this constitution.

The Wood element is ruled by the liver. The eyes are closely associated with this element. The liver is the detoxifying organ in the body, filtering all chemicals and heavy metals. Use of pesticides, medications, and toxic food will injure the liver. Most seizure problems are closely related to the liver; this element should always be supported in pets suffering seizure disorders. When unbalanced, many problems can arise including:

- Seizures

- Liver disease, hepatitis

- Gall bladder disease

- Aggression

- Cracked, brittle, or broken nails

- Tendon tears

- Ligaments tears

- Glaucoma

- Dry eye

- Conjunctivitis

Fresh green foods feed this element. Recommended foods for Wood constitution include:

✓ Chicken, beef, or pig liver

✓ Barley

✓ Dark leafy green vegetables like kale, spinach, cabbage, and mustard greens

✓ Carrots

✓ Asparagus

✓ Mushrooms

✓ Dandelion greens

✓ Citrus fruits and peels

Breeds prone to retinal degeneration or other eye diseases will benefit from the addition of:

✓ Chlorella or spirulina

✓ Eggs

✓ Foods high in lycopene – carrots, tomatoes, watermelon, red pepper, asparagus, red cabbage

✓ Foods high in lutein – asparagus, dark leafy greens, broccoli, Brussel sprouts, summer squash

Herbs that help drain the liver and resolve stagnation include:

✓ Ginger

✓ Garlic

✓ Corn silk

✓ Hawthorn

✓ Dandelion root

Avoid processed foods or foods high in cooked fats. Like feeds like; these animals should have some liver (from a clean source) in their diet.

These animals benefit from walking, exercise, and having a job.

Vitamins, minerals, and supplements to support the liver include:

✓ Milk thistle – silymarin

✓ SAMe (S-Adenosyl-Methionine)

✓ Methionine - beef, pork, fish

✓ Cysteine - beef, chicken, pork

✓ Taurine - heart, liver, kidney, eggs, fish, meat, unpasteurized goat milk

✓ Zinc – oysters, mussels

✓ Selenium - large fish, heart, barley, oats

✓ B-complex vitamins - meats, organ meats, mushrooms, dark leafy greens, eggs, raw goat milk

Liver Support Diet

This diet is good for pets with elevated liver enzymes, swollen liver, diabetes, Cushing's disease, tendon or ligament injuries, brittle nails, or seizures.

   1 pound beef cubed or ground

   2 ounces beef liver chopped or ground

   1 egg without shell (see supplement section for use of egg shells)

   8 ounces dark leafy greens (kale, collards, spinach, dandelion greens, beet greens, watercress) chopped or ground

   8 ounces pumpkin finely chopped or mashed

   2 ounces beets finely chopped or ground

   2 stalks celery finely chopped or ground

   Top with 2 canned sardines in water at the time of feeding.

This diet can be ground and mixed together, cooking at 325° F. for 30 to 45 minutes in a loaf or square baking pan, cooked on low for 4 to 6 hours in a slow cooker, or fed raw.

If you like to feed grains, add ½ cup of cooked barley before baking. If making this in a slow cooker, ¼ cup dry grain can be added at the time of preparation and allowed to cook with the other ingredients.

Good treats include freeze dried liver, heart, green tripe, or sweet potato.

Liver Draining Diet

This diet is great for pets with seizures, Cushing's disease, swollen liver or elevated liver enzymes.

1 pound chicken or turkey gizzards chopped or ground

2 ounces chicken or turkey liver chopped or ground

4 ounces butternut squash, pumpkin, or sweet potato finely chopped or processed

2 ounces dandelion greens finely chopped or ground

4 ounces asparagus finely chopped or ground

2 stalks celery finely chopped or ground

1 egg without shell (see supplement section for use of egg shells)

This diet can be ground and mixed together, cooking at 325° F. for 30 to 45 minutes in a loaf or square baking pan, cooked on low for 4 to 6 hours in a slow cooker, or fed raw.

If you like to feed grains, add ½ cup of cooked barley before baking. If making this in a slow cooker, ¼ cup dry grain can be added at the time of preparation and allowed to cook with the other ingredients.

Fermented vegetables would be a good addition to this diet at 1 teaspoon per 15 pounds body weight.

Good treats include celery, hard-boiled eggs, and green tripe.

Diet to Build Liver Blood

This diet is great for dogs with torn ACL's, dry brittle nails, dry coat with dandruff, and pale tongue.

1 pound beef, chicken, or turkey hearts chopped or ground

3 ounces beef, chicken, or turkey liver chopped or ground

3 ounces kale, spinach, and/or parsley finely chopped or processed

4 ounces sweet potato or pumpkin cooked and mashed

2 eggs without shell (see supplement section for use of egg shells)

2 teaspoons ground cinnamon

Top with 2 canned sardines in water at the time of feeding.

This diet can be ground and mixed together, cooking at 325° F. for 30 to 45 minutes in a loaf or square baking pan, cooked on low for 4 to 6 hours in a slow cooker, or fed raw.

If you like to feed grains, add ½ cup of cooked barley or brown rice before baking. If making this in a slow cooker, ¼ cup dry grain can be added at the time of preparation and allowed to cook with the other ingredients.

Good treats include green tripe, hard-boiled egg, sardines, kale chips, and freeze-dried organ meats.

Dry Eye Diet

1 pound beef chopped or ground

3 ounces beef liver chopped or ground

3 ounces beef heart chopped or ground

4 ounces spinach or kale finely chopped or ground

3 ounces carrot finely chopped or ground

1 egg without shell (see supplement section for use of egg shells)

2 ounces clams rinsed well to remove salt

1 pear chopped or ground

2 teaspoons finely ground almonds

1 tablespoon ground peppermint or spearmint

Add 2 sardines canned in water at the time of feeding.

This diet can be ground and mixed together, cooking at 325° F. for 30 to 45 minutes in a loaf or square baking pan, cooked on low for 4 to 6 hours in a slow cooker, or fed raw.

If you like to feed grains, add ½ cup of cooked barley before baking. If making this in a slow cooker, ¼ cup dry grain can be added at the time of preparation and allowed to cook with the other ingredients.

Good treats include sardines, hard-boiled eggs, carrots, pears, and freeze-dried organs.

Diet for Liver Qi Stagnation

This diet is great for dogs that are aggressive, lash out at others, or have seizures secondary to liver Qi stagnation.

   1 pound pork cubed or ground

   4 ounces crab

   2 ounces beef liver chopped or ground

   4 ounces Shiitake or Portobello mushroom finely chopped or ground

   3 ounces mustard greens finely chopped or ground

   4 ounces yellow squash finely chopped or ground

   2 tablespoons honey

   ½ teaspoon dried ground turmeric or ginger

This diet can be ground and mixed together, cooking at 325° F. for 30 to 45 minutes in a loaf or square baking pan, cooked on low for 4 to 6 hours in a slow cooker, or fed raw.

If you like to feed grains, add ½ cup of cooked barley or millet before baking. If making this in a slow cooker, ¼ cup dry grain can be added at the time of preparation and allowed to cook with the other ingredients.

Good treats include cucumber, celery, radishes, eggs, and sardines.

Liver Nodule Diet

1 pound chicken cubed or ground (can include bones if feeding raw)

3 ounces chicken liver chopped or ground

6 ounces Shiitake mushroom finely chopped or processed

8 ounces yellow squash finely chopped or processed

3 ounces radicchio or red cabbage finely chopped or processed

4 ounces cooked oats

1 ounce honey

½ tablespoon fresh ginger root finely chopped or processed

½ teaspoon dried ground coriander

½ teaspoon dried ground cardamom

This diet can be ground and mixed together, cooking at 325° F. for 30 to 45 minutes in a loaf or square baking pan, cooked on low for 4 to 6 hours in a slow cooker, or fed raw (except the oats). If making as a slow cooker meal, 2 ounces of dry oats may be used and allowed to cook with the other ingredients.

Good treats include cucumber, celery, and radishes.

METAL

Dogs in the Metal element may have a white coat and like to live in a structured environment. They may be more easily trained because they like to listen to the owner's commands and follow orders. They tend to be aloof, confident, and independent. West Highland White Terriers are a good example.

The metal element is ruled by the lungs. The lungs are the first barrier and filter for the air that is inhaled. Healthy lung function forms the first defense against cold and wind that assault the body. Skin is closely associated with lung function, as it forms the outer defensive layer for the body. When unbalanced, these animals may be prone to:

- Lung disease
- Chronic coughing
- Wheezing
- Asthma
- Nasal congestion and discharge
- Skin infections, rashes, and itching

Lungs like moisture and dislike dryness, therefore Yin tonics should be added to the diet. White foods feed this element. Recommended foods include:

✓ Eggs

✓ Duck

✓ Barley

✓ Tofu

✓ Radishes

✓ White mushrooms

✓ White meats

✓ White rice

Avoid dairy which can produce phlegm and clog the lungs. Goat or sheep products are preferable, like fermented raw goat milk, if using dairy. Honey is useful for animals that are coughing because it is a Lung Yin tonic. Like feeds like; these animals should have some lung included in their diet.

These animals benefit from brushing and stimulation of the skin and haircoat.

Diet to Support the Lung

This diet is excellent for pets with chronic cough, asthma, or respiratory symptoms.

1 pound pork or duck cubed or ground

4 ounces beef or pork kidney cubed or ground

2 ounces lung (can use freeze-dried if you cannot find fresh)

6 ounces cooked mashed sweet potato

3 ounces kale finely chopped or ground

2 tablespoons honey

1 tablespoon ground peppermint

1 pear finely chopped or ground

This diet can be ground and mixed together, cooking at 325° F. for 30 to 45 minutes in a loaf or square baking pan, cooked on low for 4 to 6 hours in a slow cooker, or fed raw.

If you like to feed grains, add ½ cup of cooked barley or white rice before baking. If making this in a slow cooker, ¼ cup dry grain can be added at the time of preparation and allowed to cook with the other ingredients.

Good treats include pieces of apricot, baked or freeze-dried lung, walnuts, and almonds.

Summer Damp Heat

Summer Damp Heat commonly causes skin infections, rashes, and itching. Cooling, draining foods can be added to the diet to combat this condition. These include:

- ✓ Barley, millet, or wheat if including grains in the diet
- ✓ Pork
- ✓ Duck
- ✓ Rabbit
- ✓ Cold water fish – sardines, mackerel, cod
- ✓ Kangaroo – drying but warm
- ✓ Celery
- ✓ Asparagus
- ✓ Turnips
- ✓ Broccoli
- ✓ Cabbage
- ✓ Squash
- ✓ Cucumber
- ✓ Zucchini
- ✓ Mushrooms
- ✓ Apples
- ✓ Pears
- ✓ Clams

Diet to Treat Skin Damp Heat

1 pound pork or rabbit cubed or ground

3 ounces pork or chicken liver chopped or ground

4 ounces butternut squash finely chopped or processed

4 ounces mixed green vegetables including cabbage, broccoli, kale, turnip, watercress finely chopped or processed

4 ounces Shiitake or Portobello mushroom finely chopped or processed

2 stalks celery chopped or processed

2 teaspoons flax seed oil

This diet can be ground and mixed together, cooking at 325° F. for 30 to 45 minutes in a loaf or square baking pan, cooked on low for 4 to 6 hours in a slow cooker, or fed raw.

If you like to feed grains, add ½ cup of cooked barley before baking. If making this in a slow cooker, ¼ cup dry grain can be added at the time of preparation and allowed to cook with the other ingredients.

Good treats include cucumber, celery, broccoli, and sardines.

Diet to Treat Skin Damp Heat Take Two

1 pound rabbit cubed or ground baked, boiled, or raw (bones can be included if feeding raw)

4 ounces beets boiled and mashed

4 ounces mixed raw romaine, cabbage, and sprouts finely chopped

4 ounces pumpkin or butternut squash boiled and mashed

1 tablespoon coconut oil

Mix all ingredients together and serve. If you wish to add grains, add ½ cup cooked barley.

Good treats include cucumber, apple, pear, celery, and freeze-dried lung.

Diet to Treat Skin Damp Heat Take Three

1 pound white fish (cod, tilapia, flounder, sardine, mackerel, anchovy) baked and de-boned

8 ounces yellow squash finely chopped or processed

6 ounces string beans finely chopped or processed

4 ounces Shiitake or Portobello mushroom chopped or processed

1 tablespoon coconut oil

Vegetables may be processed, mixed with coconut oil, and served raw or may be sautee'd in coconut oil. Serve vegetables and fish together. If you wish to add grains, add ½ cup cooked barley.

Good treats include cucumber, apple, pear, celery, and freeze-dried lung.

Diet to Treat Dry Skin

1 pound beef or pork cubed or ground

3 ounces beef or pork liver chopped or ground

3 ounces beef or pork heart cubed or ground

1 egg without shell (see supplement section for use of egg shells)

4 ounces kale, spinach, or collards finely chopped or processed

2 carrots grated or processed

4 ounces sweet potato, pumpkin, or butternut squash finely chopped or processed

Add 2 sardines canned in water at the time of feeding.

This diet can be ground and mixed together, cooking at 325° F. for 30 to 45 minutes in a loaf or square baking pan, cooked on low for 4 to 6 hours in a slow cooker, or fed raw.

If you like to feed grains, add ½ cup of cooked millet before baking. If making this in a slow cooker, ¼ cup dry grain can be added at the time of preparation and allowed to cook with the other ingredients.

Good treats include dates, figs, freeze-dried lung, and eggs.

Cancer – Is There Hope?

No one ever wants to hear the diagnosis. Sometimes owners suspect something is very wrong; other times the bad news comes as a complete shock. It will take time to process the information, but then you must move forward. Whether you decide to seek advice and treatment from an oncologist is your choice. Either way, changes to the diet can make a huge impact on the health and vitality of your pet.

There are changes that should be made to give your pet a better chance at fighting this dreaded disease. Recently, ketogenic diets have been in the news as a way to greatly improve the chances for survival. I will not discuss ketogenic diets here; instead I recommend reading the information provided by The KetoPet Sanctuary on their website www.ketopetsanctuary.org. Dr. Ian Billinghurst has also written an in-depth discussion on the causes and treatment of cancer, *Pointing the Bone at Cancer*, which I highly recommend. It is available on my website in the U.S. at www.drjudymorgan.com and his website, www.drianbillinghurst. com in Australia.

Over the years, scientists and nutritionists have shown that cancer cells use sugars as their main source of energy. There has recently been more debate over the role that fats play in the spread of malignant cancer cells; unfortunately, there is not enough research available to do more than speculate. Based on the knowledge available, we do know that sugar must be minimized in the diet.

Carbohydrates are basically a form of sugar. The worst forms of sugar for cancer patients are the refined grains like white rice and products made with processed white flour. Natural sugars may also be found in dairy products, fruits, and vegetables. All grains and legumes are carbohydrates. Grain-free processed canned and dry pet foods are not carbohydrate-free and will not suffice. Grains in these products have been replaced with alternative carbohydrate sources such as peas, lentils, potatoes, and tapioca.

A second energy source required by cancer cells is an amino acid called glutamine. Glutamine is found in high quantities in red meats, dairy products, and wheat. Glutamine is also used in digestive supplements for inflammatory bowel disease and leaky gut. Avoid these supplements if your pet has cancer.
By decreasing the amount of sugar and glutamine in the diet, the cancer cells have less energy available to grow and multiply.

Healthy carbohydrates that might be considered for these pets include pumpkin, varieties of squash, and perhaps some sweet potato. I do not use grains for my cancer patients, but if anorexia becomes a problem, low glycemic grains such as barley (cooling) or oats (warming) may be considered.

Butter, coconut oil, and organic olive oil are good fats that may be added for extra calories, if needed. Fresh garlic, a sprinkling of parmesan cheese, and bone broth may entice pets to eat when they are having a bad day. Soups, teas, and meals in the slow cooker may be easier to digest.

Dyes, chemicals, pesticides, preservatives, and fats cooked at high temperatures must be eliminated from the diet, as these can contribute to inflammation. Organic locally raised food will be the best source of nutrition for your pet with cancer.

Obesity creates inflammation in the body. If your pet is overweight you need to get serious about getting off the extra pounds. Increase exercise if your pet is still strong enough to do so.

Additions to the diet can be made to help fight cancer cells.

Cruciferous vegetables contain chemicals called glucosinolates that have been shown to help prevent and combat cancer.

- They help protect cells from DNA damage.

- They help inactivate carcinogens.

- They have antiviral and antibacterial properties.

- They have anti-inflammatory effects.

- They cause death of cancer cells.

- They inhibit tumor blood vessel formation and tumor cell migration needed for metastasis or spread.

Cannabidiol, or CBD oil, has become a popular addition to the treatment regimen for pets with cancer. Legal, regulated, commercial products are available; they contain less than 0.3% THC, which is the psychoactive compound in cannabis, or marijuana. While some people are touting the benefits of whole marijuana for pets, this is not legal in any state. Pets are susceptible to side effects, including death, when given too much THC.

From a TCVM standpoint, most cancers fall into a few categories. They may be associated with phlegm and stagnation, which create nodules or masses. Pets with this disorder may have a dark or lavender tongue with a white coating. Foods that dissolve phlegm and resolve stagnation should be part of the diet. Cancer may also be secondary to blood deficiency. These pets may have a lighter tongue, weak pulses, dry skin with flaking, dry pads, and a dry nose. Feeding blood tonics will build blood, but be sure to include ingredients that move stagnation.

Many cancers are associated with excess heat, or Yang. These pets will have increased thirst, increased panting, and a dark red tongue. By choosing diets that include Yin tonics throughout the book, it is possible to address these constitutional issues.

Digestive function and kidney function must always be addressed. Without strong digestion (Spleen function), the immune system will be weakened. Jing tonics are important ingredients for these pets.

Supplements I like to include: CoQ10, milk thistle to restore the liver, medicinal mushrooms, chlorella, omega 3's, colostrum, and herbs specific to the cancer. If your pet is undergoing chemotherapy, please speak with your oncologist before adding any supplements, as some may interfere with the drugs being used.

My Cancer Fighting Veggie Grind

I add this to every meal for our dogs. This makes a lot, so feel free to decrease quantities used.

- 1 head red or green cabbage
- 1 head cauliflower
- 2 heads broccoli
- 1 bunch asparagus
- 1 cup or one bunch parsley
- 1 bunch celery
- 5 cloves garlic
- 8 ounces kale
- 8 ounces Brussel sprouts
- 8 ounces Shiitake mushrooms
- 1 cucumber with peel
- 1 whole lemon including seeds and peel
- 1 red pepper
- 1 medium sized beet
- 4 ounces blueberries
- ½ cup flax seed

Grind all ingredients together. Freeze in small portions. Add ½ teaspoon per ten pounds body weight to each meal. If your pet already has cancer, and you want to keep sugars lower, omit the beet, red pepper, cucumber, and blueberries. If your pet develops loose stools or excessive gas, decrease amount fed.

208

Golden Paste

Turmeric is a root herb that has been studied extensively for its cancer and inflammation-fighting properties. Most of the effect is due to an ingredient called curcumin. It is a powerful anti-oxidant and Qi tonic, reducing stagnation and pain; it has been used to decrease inflammation associated with heart disease, back pain, and arthritis. Studies have shown it may decrease the risk of getting cancer, as well as helping to treat cancer.

Turmeric is not very well absorbed when eaten, but the absorption is increased when it is taken with black pepper.

1 cup warm water

½ cup organic turmeric root powder

1/3 cup organic coconut oil OR 1/3 cup bone broth

½ tablespoon organic freshly ground black pepper

1 tablespoon organic Ceylon cinnamon

Place turmeric powder and water in a small saucepan on low heat on the stovetop. Stir until it forms a paste, usually about 5 minutes. Remove from heat and add the pepper and cinnamon, stirring to mix. Add coconut oil or bone broth and stir well.

Store in an airtight container in the refrigerator and use within two weeks. It can be frozen. Mix ¼ teaspoon for small dogs and up to 1 tablespoon for large dogs in each meal.

Healthy Diet

1 pound chicken chopped or ground with skin (bone can be included if feeding raw)

3 ounces chicken liver

3 ounces chicken heart

4 ounces yellow squash chopped or processed

¼ cup veggie grind

1 egg without shell (see supplement section for use of egg shells)

2 sardines canned in water

¼ cup bone broth

Mix all ingredients together and serve raw. If you do not want to feed raw, mix all ingredients in a sauce pan. Gently sauté in 1 tablespoon coconut oil or sesame oil.

Healthy Diet Take Two

1 pound wild caught salmon, gently cooked and deboned

3 ounces organic kale finely chopped or processed

4 ounces Shiitake mushrooms finely chopped or processed

1 egg without shell (see supplement section for use of egg shells)

1 tablespoon organic coconut oil

Mix all ingredients together and serve. Vegetables and egg may be gently cooked if desired.

Healthy Diet Take Three

1 pound deboned white fish (cod, sardine, mackerel) gently cooked on stove top in 1 tablespoon butter

4 ounces Shiitake mushrooms chopped or processed

4 ounces broccoli chopped or processed

1 teaspoon fresh ginger root grated

Vegetables may be lightly cooked with fish if desired. Mix all ingredients together and serve.

216

Healthy Diet Take Four

1 pound rabbit ground or chopped (can include bone if feeding raw)

3 ounces rabbit organ mix chopped or ground

4 ounces green beans chopped or processed

4 ounces white mushrooms chopped or processed

4 ounces yellow squash chopped or processed

Mix all ingredients together. Can be fed raw, baked in a loaf pan or square pan at 325° F for 30 to 45 minutes, or cooked on low heat in the slow cooker for four hours. Alternatively, the meat and organs can be gently baked at 325° F on a baking sheet for 25 to 30 minutes, then mixed with raw processed vegetables.

Quick Meal

4 cans wild caught sardines in water

2 eggs raw or over easy, leaving yolk runny (hard boiled last resort)

¼ cup veggie grind

½ tablespoon organic coconut oil

Mix all ingredients together and serve.

Home-made Treats

With eight to ten dogs in our home at any given time, we generally do not hand out a lot of treats. But most pet owners enjoy being able to give rewards or have treats for training. Unfortunately, the processed pet treat industry is a minefield that many pet owners do not know how to navigate. There are very few purchased treats I would consider giving my pets. If you are interested in using processed treats, check my website which will show some healthy options. If it's on my site, I would feed it to my own pets. You can save money and be sure of quality by making your own treats.

Fresh fruits and vegetables make great treats. Dates, figs, all sorts of melons, berries, bananas, pineapple, pears, apples, carrots, cucumber, celery, broccoli, and small pieces of meat are excellent additions to the diet. Offer your pet different options; you may be surprised at their choices!

224

Dehydrated Treats

Most people do not own a dehydrator. There is really no need to invest in one if you own an oven. Dehydrated treats are very simple to make.

Cut strips of meat, liver, kidney, lung, heart, tripe, sweet potato, apple, pineapple, banana, green beans, mango, papaya, or whatever ingredient you need to support your pet's constitution and personality.
All pieces should be about ¼ inch thick, but can be as long and wide as you choose.

Place the strips or pieces on a wire rack placed on a cookie sheet.

Slide the tray into the oven and set at 170° F. Allow the trays to stay in the oven overnight for about 8 to 12 hours. In the morning, remove from the oven and blot any excess moisture with a paper towel. Allow to cool. Dehydrated treats should be stored in an airtight container in the refrigerator and used within a week. They can also be frozen and thawed as needed.

Ginger Cookies with Cinnamon

Cream together:

¾ cup butter

¼ cup molasses

1 egg

Combine:

2 ¼ cups almond flour

2 teaspoons dry ginger

¾ teaspoon dry cinnamon

¼ teaspoon salt

Add dry ingredients to wet ingredients, mixing well. Roll into 1 ½ inch balls and place on cookie sheet. Bake at 350° F. for 10 to 12 minutes. Makes 2 to 3 dozen.

Antioxidant, Blood Tonic Liver Fruit Cake

1 pound chicken, turkey, or beef liver – ground in food processor or with grinder attachment for stand mixer

½ cup organic blueberries

½ cup organic cranberries

½ cup chopped parsley

1 egg without shell

¾ cup coconut or almond flour

Mix all ingredients together. Oil small loaf pans with extra virgin olive oil. Pour mixed ingredients into small loaf pans. Bake at 350° F. for about 30 minutes, depending on size of pan. It should be firm to the touch when finished. Allow to cool then slice into bite size pieces and serve! Refrigerate unused portions and use within 5 to 7 days. Unused portions can be frozen and thawed before feeding.

Cranberry Applesauce Coconut Cookies

1 cup applesauce (organic, no sugar, or make your own by cooking peeled apples in a small amount of water in a saucepan on the stove.)

1 cup lightly chopped cranberries

2 cups coconut flour

1 teaspoon cinnamon

1 egg

Mix all ingredients together. Drop by rounded teaspoons on parchment paper on cookie sheet. Bake at 350° F for 10 to 15 minutes. Makes about 4 dozen. Store in airtight container in the refrigerator for 4 to 5 days or freeze and thaw as needed.

Sesame Kale Chips

1 bunch kale, large stems removed

1 tablespoon olive oil or melted coconut oil

1 tablespoon sesame seeds

Lightly toss pieces of kale in organic olive oil and sesame seeds. Place on parchment paper on a cookie sheet. Bake at 300° F for 10 to 15 minutes, rotate the pan and cook an additional 10 to 15 minutes until edges are brown, but not burnt. Remove from oven and allow to cool on baking sheet. Store in airtight container.

SUPPLEMENTS – BALANCING ACT

While I don't feel that every meal needs to be complete and balanced, I do feel diets should be balanced over time. There are some critical nutrients that need to be addressed in order to accomplish this.

Calcium – Most meats and grains are higher in phosphorous than calcium. Dogs and cats require a calcium to phosphorous ratio of around 1.2 to 1. To achieve that ratio, a calcium supplement must be added. There are several ways to do this:

- Include ground bone in the raw meal at a rate of about 10% of the meal. Raw fed dogs commonly have meaty bones added to the diet to provide this nutrient. Adding excess bone will result in constipation and impaction.

- Add a mineral supplement made for balancing home prepared meals. A general vitamin/mineral supplement will not contain enough calcium! Approximately 750 to 1000 mg calcium must be added to each pound of meat in the diet. There are many on the market, derived from different sources such as bone meal or seabed calcium.

- Ground eggshell can provide calcium. The shells should be dried, then finely ground. A coffee bean grinder works well for this. Approximately ½ teaspoon per pound of meat will provide sufficient calcium.

- Microcrystalline Hydroxyapatite is another calcium source, made in New Zealand. Be sure to use a product with no added vitamin D.

Iodine and trace minerals – kelp, spirulina, and blue-green algae are a good source of these minerals. Small and medium size dogs only need 1/8th teaspoon every day or every other day, large dogs ¼ teaspoon. These minerals may also be found in some of the commercial mineral mixes with calcium. A natural source would be oysters or mussels. Large dogs can suffice with one oyster or mussel per day; smaller dogs can have smaller portions or be fed this ingredient every other day.

Salt – This is an important mineral that is often overlooked. Sodium and chloride are essential for life. A pinch of salt added to each recipe will suffice. I like sea salt; do not use iodized salts. For dogs in heart failure or on diuretics, salt substitutes containing potassium chloride work well, as these dogs tend to have low potassium levels.

Vitamin D – This vitamin is found in egg yolks and fish in high quantities. Dogs should have eggs or fish included in their diet four to five days each week. Daily is also fine. Studies have shown dogs with heart or kidney disease have low vitamin D levels. Supplementation with vitamin D3 may be necessary. Avoid over-supplementation. Your veterinarian can send a blood sample to the lab to test your pet's vitamin D levels. Most pets require about 25 IU per pound of body weight; human vitamin D3 supplements are usually too concentrated for pet use.

Vitamin E – This vitamin should be added to the diet. Pure wheat germ oil (not an oil blend) is a natural source of vitamin E and can be added to the diet at ¼ teaspoon for small dogs under 30 pounds, ½ teaspoon for medium dogs up to 60 pounds, and 1 teaspoon daily for large dogs. If giving capsule form, dogs under 10 pounds should receive a 100 IU capsule every other day. Dogs 11 to 35 pounds can be given 100 units daily or 200 IU every other day. Dogs 36 to 75 pounds can be given 400 IU every other day. Dogs over 75 pounds need 300 IU daily. They will require more vitamin E if they are being given large quantities of omega 3 fatty acids. Check the omega 3 supplement you are using to see if it contains vitamin E.

Omega 3 fatty acids – These will be higher in grass fed meats and wild caught fish than animals that have been factory farmed. Omega 3's have been shown to decrease inflammation; they are very useful for skin, joint, and heart disease. Generally, I give 30 to 40 mg per pound of body weight per day. Pets with Spleen Qi deficiency and poor digestion will commonly develop diarrhea when given amounts this high. Warm the digestion and drain damp if this occurs. Flax seed oil is not a significant source of omega 3 for dogs.

Cod Liver Oil – This may be very high in vitamin A. If using this oil, look for brands that have undergone molecular distillation to remove the vitamins.

CoQ10 – This powerful antioxidant is a mainstay for my dogs. Production in the body decreases with age; this enzyme is required for the cells to function. It helps protect the heart from inflammation, may decrease risk of cancer, improves functioning of the immune system, and helps prevent cognitive dysfunction. General supplementation is recommended at 1 mg per pound of body weight, although I use 100 mg daily for my 20-pound dogs. Side effects are rare, with loose stools being seen occasionally with very high doses.

Probiotics – These are the beneficial bacteria in the gut. Natural sources include fermented vegetables and fermented milk. There are many probiotic powders and capsules available on the market. If using a powder or capsule, avoid anything with Animal Digest or sugars as the base ingredient.

Specific supplements for each organ system are discussed in further detail in my book *From Needles to Natural*.

PUTTING IT ALL TOGETHER

I readily admit, when I began making meals for my dogs, I was scared. I heard so many naysayers with doomsday prophecies of diets lacking the right combination of protein, fat, carbohydrates, vitamins and minerals; I didn't think I could possibly prepare food that would be as nutritious as the complete and balanced kibble in a bag. Luckily, my professional journey allowed me to discover the hidden secrets of the processed pet food industry, forcing me to take a leap of faith toward making meals for my dogs. The incredible changes I saw in my own dogs, and later my patients, proved to me that fresh food gives rise to good health.

When I started cooking and designing diets, the symptoms of allergies, arthritis, and chronic inflammatory diseases disappeared. Owners were amazed at the changes in their dogs, as their pets became more mobile, had shinier coats, and black patent leather noses. They were more engaged and seemed to be happier. Patients with horrible diagnoses, given days to weeks to live, were suddenly beating the odds, and living from months to years. Watching the changes as they occurred brought me a level of joy that I hadn't experienced in all my years of veterinary practice.

Making food for dogs is not rocket science; you don't have to be a master chef to prepare meals for them. It gets easier - I promise. I've coached pet owners who had never boiled water and could barely make toast. Some have taken cooking classes so they can prepare meals for their dogs, where many clients have started preparing healthier meals for themselves because they started preparing meals for their dogs. My mother never enjoyed cooking; I thought she would never cook for her dog. Then one day I smelled puploaf in the oven when I walked into her home. She wanted her dog to have the best nutrition possible.

You don't need to invest in fancy equipment to get the job done, although after you begin preparing meals, you may find yourself admiring fancy grinders on the internet. Our kitchen is equipped with more gadgets than I ever imagined owning, but we could easily make do with a sharp knife, a cutting board, and a few bowls and pans. Start slowly, build your confidence, and discover the ingredients your dog likes and dislikes. Eventually you'll be able to design meals, substituting healing ingredients as needed.

Food is the foundation of life for all species. The principles of Chinese medicine food therapy apply to dogs, cats, horses, and humans. Changing diets based on personality, illness, and season will help you and your pets live a more balanced, healthy life. I've given you the knowledge to move forward. Now it's time to take the first step.

Ralf P. La Belle (Kayak Schlebelle) was kind enough to send photos of the meals prepared for his three rescued dogs, Keysha, Struga and Willow. I am not suggesting you need to plate your doggy dinners this elaborately, but the photos were so awesome I had to share.

Chicken drumstick topped with sliced summer squash and Monarda flower petals, Lamb with a spinach and kale pesto, Sardine with a blend of chopped green beans and summer squash, Organic egg, Beef kidney, Organic blueberries, Beef heart, Sorrel and parsley on top of venison steak

Chopped chicken drumstick, Beef heart with baby romaine leaves, Thin sliced beef steak topped with ground pumpkin seed and a side of our Green Willow (a variety of kale, spinach, carrot, garlic, ginger, lemon juice, turmeric, parsley, celery), Beef kidney, Mango watermelon and raspberries with kefir, Sliced beef tongue and organic egg in center of dish

Sardine, Shredded zucchini, Organic egg, Sliced beef with green beans, Plantain leaves and mint blossom, Beef liver, Broccoli, Lamb topped with kefir and blueberries, Chicken drumstick topped with Monarda flower petals

Green bean summer squash beef roulade, Beef heart and herb medallions, Zucchini egg cup, Kidney, Deer tripe, Watermelon blueberry kefir, Chicken drumstick, VH6 Paste, Roasted beet strips, and Green garnishes (dandelion leavves, plantain, and parsley)

CPSIA information can be obtained
at www.ICGtesting.com
Printed in the USA
BVHW021212080719
552849BV00031B/2079/P